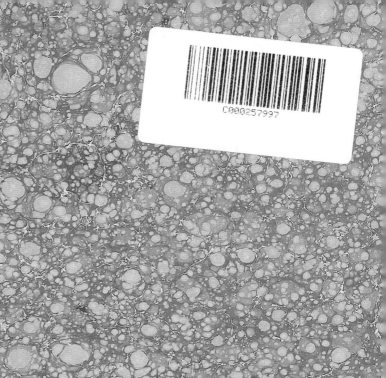

THE MODERN SHERLOCK HOLMES
An Introduction to Forensic Science Today

THE MODERN
SHERLOCK HOLMES
An Introduction to Forensic Science Today

By Judy Williams

The Modern Sherlock Holmes is based on the BBC World Service
Series: *The Modern Sherlock Holmes* produced by Ruth Linton and
broadcast in February and November 1991.

First published in Great Britain in 1991
by Broadside Books Ltd
2 Gurney Rd, London E15 1SH

Designed by Emma Axbey and Glen Coombes
The Studio
15 Soho Square London W1

Typeset by BP Integraphics, Upper Bristol Rd. Bath

Printed by Eagle Colourbooks, Glasgow

ISBN: 0 951 5629-3-2

Acknowledgements

Great thanks are due to the following forensic specialists and institutions who were unstintingly generous with their time and help in the preparation of this book:

Dr. David Barclay and Dr. Peter Clarke of the *Forensic Science Service* Priory House, Gooch St. N. Birmingham. *The Forensic Science Service* is an executive agency of the Home Office providing assistance to the Criminal Justice System of England and Wales in over 60,000 individual crimes per year. It is also a research unit and provides a central database service for forensic laboratories worldwide.

Professor Alan Usher, Professor Michael Green and Mr. David Jarvis at the *Medico Legal Centre*, 3 Watery St. Sheffield. The Medico – Legal Centre is Britain's first purpose-built research and crime investigation centre, containing a Public Mortuary, Coroner's Court and Forensic Pathology department. It investigates around 1,000 deaths annually in the North and South Yorkshire and Humberside region.

Special thanks are also due to:

Mr. David Carter, Dr. Martin Hall and Dr. George Else at the dept. of Entomology, Natural History Museum, London.

Dr Zakaria Erzinclioglu of the Department of Zoology, Cambridge.

Mr. Ray Ruddick, Consultant Photographer and Mr. Bernard Sims, Hon. Senior Lecturer at the Dept. of Forensic Medicine, London Hospital Medical College.

Mr. Roger Summers, Head of Photographics at the Derbyshire Constabulary.

Mr. Tom Warlow of the Hinching Brooke Park Firearms Laboratory, Huntingdon.

Contents

Forensic Science
in the 1990's

The workings of the Forensic Science Service are something of a mystery to most people. Occasionally the existence of the organisation is brought to our notice by some spectacular success or failure, but generally we remain ignorant of what goes on in the forensic science laboratory. This book is intended to dispel some of the mystery. Although it does contain some sensational case histories, it also focuses on the more mundane aspects of the forensic scientist's work, and on the technical advances which have made much of that work possible.

The Forensic Science Service in Britain is a part of the Home Office, and its 450 scientists are therefore completely independent of the police: the scientists are based in six operational laboratories across England and Wales, plus one establishment devoted solely to research, and together they handle over 60,000 cases a year. The Metropolitan Police force runs an additional laboratory which is not part of the service. Forensic pathology is a separate area, and pathologists are not directly employed by the Home Office; they usually work in a University or N.H.S. hospital, and are called upon as necessary to deal with forensic cases. Over three quarters of cases which go to the laboratories concern drunken driving or drugs offences, and most of these are relatively straightforward; the remaining cases cover a wide range, including murder, assault, theft, arson, shootings, explosions and forgery. The job of the Forensic Science Service is to give impartial advice about such offences, based on the available evidence. It is usually the more serious cases which are referred to the laboratory, and because this help is often only sought when normal police investigations have reached a dead end, a great deal can hang on the forensic scientist's report.

According to a Home Office study, over half the cases each year involve matching different items or substances to a common source: this might mean showing that a single fibre came originally from a certain piece of clothing, or matching a suspect's blood group with bloodstains found at the scene of a crime. A further third of cases call for the identification of a particular substance, perhaps to show that petrol had been used to start a fire. Less than ten per cent of the laboratory's work involves searching through a collection of suspect items in search of clues, without a specific aim. Forensic scientists are therefore dependent on the information and evidence they receive from the scene of a crime, and they cannot produce answers from out of thin air. Unfortunately, there is a general perception that this is exactly what forensic science does – sophisticated and sensitive tests often appear to pluck information from nowhere, and the very skill with which some cases are solved can foster the mysterious image surrounding the forensics department. Both the police and the public often have unrealistic expectations of the abilities of the Forensic Science Service, which only lead to disappointment when the scientists do not live up to these expectations. When it is technically impossible to prove something, or when a scientist is shown to be fallible, our faith in the integrity and usefulness of the whole organisation is, somewhat unreasonably, shaken.

During the hunt for Peter Sutcliffe, the 'Yorkshire Ripper', there were many complaints that the length of time it took to catch him enabled Sutcliffe to carry on with his campaign of murder. But the search was complicated by two factors, which turned out to have nothing to do with the case, but which had to be fully examined nonetheless. Firstly, a hoaxer sent the police some tapes, on which he claimed to be responsible for the Yorkshire Ripper's crimes. Experts were agreed that the voice on the tapes had a Geordie accent, so police enquiries were deflected to the Wearside area for some time – quite erroneously, as it turned out. The second problem was posed by the murder of two women, one in Preston and one in Manchester, which were thought to be part of the Ripper's series of killings. The murderer in these cases, like Sutcliffe, was a rare 'B-secretor' (his 'B' blood group could be identified from secretions in other body fluids) – but when Sutcliffe was eventually caught, he strongly denied killing the two women. These apparent leads had to be followed up at the time, but both in fact proved a hindrance to the main enquiry. The forensic scientists performed the tasks asked of them, by identifying the blood groups of the samples they were given and correctly saying that they could have come from the same person; but they were not responsible for the fact that a chance correspondence of two people's blood groups pointed the police in the wrong direction.

Research has shown, however, that the input of the forensic science laboratory is more often useful than not – though this does not mean that forensic evidence always backs up the police view of a case. When a suspect has already been charged before a forensic report is sought, the result contributes to the prosecution evidence in about three quarters of cases; but about five percent of suspects are cleared completely by forensic evidence. In one case, a woman was raped in her home, and she identified a man who had access to the house as her attacker. However, forensic tests on samples from the scene of the crime and this suspect showed that he was of the wrong blood group. Eventually, another man was arrested, and he pleaded guilty to the offence. Without the forensic evidence, the first suspect might very well have been imprisoned for a crime he could not have committed.

Still, it is a fact that Home Office forensic scientists usually provide information for the prosecution rather than the defence. (There is a small body of independent firms whose scientists act for the defence side, and as they are generally staffed by ex-members of the Forensic Science Service, they are well-placed to interpret and question the official findings, if necessary.) Forensic pathologists can also just as easily appear for the defence as the prosecution, because they are primarily employed by Universities or hospitals, not by the Home Office. But all forensic scientists would strongly resist any pressure put on them to confirm the police view of a case, if the facts did not support that view. In court, the prosecution may emphasise any points in favour of their case, but no-one would try to stop a scientist putting forward any other facts which might support the defence case. In any event, it is rare for a whole case to be built upon the report of a forensic scientist alone; this usually forms no more than one link in the chain of evidence against a defendant.

Although some police officers feel that forensic scientists may be over-cautious, in discarding what appear to be good sources of evidence, the scientists are probably only trying to guard against cases failing in court when the forensic evidence is challenged. One such instance concerned a burglary at a football supporters' club, where a window was smashed and a quantity of beer was taken. The police traced the stolen beer to the owner of a nearby house, and when the forensic department examined the man's clothes, they found three fragments of glass which matched the broken window at the club. Unfortunately, the forensic scientists in charge of the case did not know that a detective had gone straight from the scene of the burglary to the suspect's house – and in court the defence claimed that the slivers of glass could have been inadvertently transferred from the police officer to the suspect. The judge ordered the forensic evidence to be ignored, and the defendant was acquitted. An instance like this, where a case was lost on forensic evidence through no fault of the scientists themselves, lowers the morale of the service, and makes the forensics experts more likely to reject any unsure evidence.

There have, however, been a series of recently reviewed trials in which the forensic evidence was found to be at fault; notably cases involving terrorist bombings, like the Birmingham Six affair. The forensic scientists cannot, of course, be held responsible for any confessions which may have been forced from the suspects in such cases, but they have been widely blamed for the results of their chemical tests to show traces of explosives, some of which have since been contested, or wholly invalidated. In defence of the scientists, and without going into detail, it must be remembered that they were using what was 'state of the art' technology at the time, and it is somewhat unfair to criticise them for working within the limits of contemporary knowledge. Scientific advances have come thick and fast in the last twenty years, and it is hardly surprising that equipment and methods used in the mid 1970s have now been superseded by more sensitive and accurate tests. Thin layer chromatography, the method used to test for small quantities of explosives on suspected terrorists in the 1970s, was the accepted standard test throughout the U.K. and the United States, and although it is now known to be less reliable than the GCMS (gas chromatography mass spectrometry) test, such improved equipment was simply not available then. At present, a Royal Commission is enquiring into various areas of criminal justice, including the use of forensic evidence in such cases, but whatever new guidelines or legislation result, it will never be possible to anticipate the scientific developments of the future.

It might be added that improved forensic methods have also recently helped uncover foul play on the part of a few members of the police force; a modern technique which reveals faint indentations in sheets of paper to sequence several pages in the right order has revealed that, in the past, some police officers inserted pages containing false confessions into long statements made by suspects. This technique has already cast doubt on the validity of confessions made by the Birmingham Six and the Guildford Four, and several other convictions are now being reconsidered, especially cases where a confession provided the only evidence for the prosecution.

For the future, efforts are being made to ensure that forensic reports are not only accurate, but also comprehensible to non-scientists; in most cases, forensic scientists do not appear in court, but their reports are submitted to the jury, so it is important that the often highly technical evidence can be easily understood. The increasing use of computers and automated tests not only reduces the possibility of human error, but also ensures that the results of the tests are recorded and stored in a permanent and easily accessible form. There is also increasing access for independent scientists to inspect the equipment and results of the Forensic Science Service; indeed, from 1991 the service will itself become an independent agency, offering its expertise for sale to all.

Professor Michael Green, a consultant pathologist to the Home Office and Professor of Forensic Pathology at the University of Sheffield put the case for his profession like this:

"no system is perfect, and the increased degree of scrutiny being brought to bear on the work of forensic scientists will strengthen and safeguard the service they offer. It will never be possible to eliminate all chance of error or misjudgement, but the Forensic Science Service strives to do the greatest good for the greatest number, for the greatest part of the time".

This book shows how forensic scientists go about this vital task.

CHAPTER ONE

Sherlock Holmes and the History of Forensic Science

The character of Sherlock Holmes first appeared in the Strand Magazine in 1891, and at once became legendary for the astounding deductive skills which helped him solve the most baffling cases. His friend Dr. Watson and the police could only watch in amazement as Holmes plucked the truth from a tangled mesh of clues, apparently aided only by a magnifying glass and the power of his intellect. Today's real-life detectives rely on forensic scientists specialising in separate areas to unravel the clues they find, using increasingly sophisticated laboratory techniques and expensive equipment. The word 'forensic' comes from the latin 'forum', where the Romans held their courts, and forensic science simply means the application of science in helping the courts arrive at the truth.

It might seem that there is little connection between the world of Holmes the fictional detective and that of the modern investigators – indeed, today's forensic scientists often deny any similarity between Holmes' methods and their own – but this is based on a misconception of the way Holmes worked. He did not solve his cases by inspired guesswork or intuition, but by a combination of careful examination, hard work and logic, just like the present day forensic scientist, to arrive at a conclusion based more often than not on a balance of probabilities pointing to the guilt or innocence of the suspect.

Above all, Holmes only worked with facts, and refused to make guesses from insufficient information: when Dr. Watson asked what he made of a mysterious note which had just arrived, Holmes replied "I have no data yet. It is a capital mistake to theorize before one has data. Insensibly one begins to twist facts to suit theories instead of theories to suit facts" (A *Scandal in Bohemia*). The modern forensics experts would certainly approve of such a cautious attitude.

Sherlock Holmes' methods were based on observation of people and things, and he was always adamant that the scene

You did not know where to look, and so you missed all that was important. I can never bring you to realize the importance of sleeves, the suggestiveness of thumb-nails, or the great issues that may hang from a bootlace.

(A CASE OF IDENTITY)

of a mystery should be left exactly as it was until he could examine it. He would visit the scene to look for traces like footprints, cigarette ash or loose threads left by the perpetrator, which would tell him where and how things had happened. When he returned to his rooms at Baker Street, he would carry out chemical tests. And he kept a huge index of all his past cases, so that he could locate a reference to a criminal or a method instantly. Today, forensic scientists still visit the scene of crime, if possible, to observe and collect the clues in their original positions. They examine evidence in the laboratory and submit it to various scientific tests. And they, too, consult a wide range of reference material, from official collections of drugs and firearms to the modern computer databases containing details of fingerprints and DNA profiles.

The Egyptians

Although the different areas of expertise which we now call forensic science had their beginnings in the rush of scientific developments of the middle of the nineteenth century, there are many examples from much earlier times of practices which would now come within the field. Most cultures have recognised that there should be some way of examining the circumstances surrounding suspicious deaths, for example, but until scientific knowledge caught up with this need, the results of such enquiries were likely to be erratic. The ancient Egyptians developed a system for telling whether a death was natural or not, but despite their skill in embalming mummies, their understanding of medicine and anatomy was not great. It is doubtful whether the answers they reached were accurate.

An image of Ta-bes, an Egyptian mummy dating from 900 B.C., built up from X-ray data and without opening her painted coffin.

Our teeth grow and sustain damage in individual ways, and because they are the part of the body which lasts the longest after death, they have long been used for identification purposes in the living and the dead. Nine hundred years ago, the impressions of teeth were used in wax seals as a legal form of personal identification. In addition, for thousands of years people have made quite skillful repairs to teeth, which has made the recognition of particular bodies easier. In a tomb dating from 2500 BC at Giza in Egypt, two molar teeth were found linked together by gold wire. This simple method of strengthening loose teeth by binding them with gold wire to firm ones was also described by the Roman physician Celsus in 32 BC.

Dental Evidence

An early case in which dental evidence of this kind helped to con-clusively identify a body occurred in America in 1775. Dr. Joseph Warren was killed in the battle of Bunker Hill in Boston, and buried in a mass grave. Dr. Paul Revere had previously made a denture for him, consisting of an ivory and silver bridge, and when the grave was opened, Dr. Revere was able to identify Dr. Warren's body by the presence of this denture. Similarly, in November 1835, Hatfield House in England burned to the ground with the Countess of Salisbury trapped inside. The ruins were searched for four-teen days, until a few bones were found in the ashes, including a jawbone. Still fixed to this were the gold attachments which had held the Countess' artificial teeth, proving the burned remains to be hers.

Casts of the teeth can often help to identify bodies, or trace the perpetrators of bite wounds.

Poisoning

Since prehistoric times, mankind has been aware of the poisonous properties of various plants and minerals, and early records show that much was known about the actions and uses of poisons and venoms. When the Greek philosopher Socrates was executed in 339 BC, he was made to take a poisonous drink made from hemlock. But while the poisonous effects of many substances were well-docu-mented, as in the natural history of plants written by Theophrastus in 300 BC, it was not until the nineteenth century that the presence of poisons could be detected in a dead body. Until the last century, it was only possible to deduce that someone had been poisoned by observing the course of their illness, but the symptoms were often indistinguishable from those of natural diseases. Poisoning with arsenic causes vomiting, diarrhoea and a weak pulse, but these are also the symptoms of a ruptured gastric ulcer.

There were many false ideas concerning signs of poisoning, for example that the body would be blue or black in colour, or that the heart of a victim would not be damaged by fire. Unfortunately for the investigator of a death, most poisons do not cause visible changes on the surface of the body or in the internal organs, and so chemical tests of the body tissues are needed to prove the presence of a toxic substance. The first such test did not exist until 1836, when James Marsh developed his test for arsenic, which could detect the absorbed poison in the organs and the blood. Marsh's test was particularly welcome because the use of arsenic for murder was very common; it was employed so frequently to get rid of unwanted relatives that it acquired the nickname 'inheritance powder'.

Early Forensic Photography

The middle of the nineteenth century saw many advances in science and technology which could be applied to forensic investigations. Discoveries in the field of chemistry provided new techniques for analysing chemical evidence, and at last a wide range of poisons could be detected in the body. The potential of the microscope was being realised; in Europe and America amateur scientists formed microscopy societies and published their discoveries about the microscopic composition of soil, blood and pond water. The police could turn to such groups for help in investigating small traces of evidence.

The development of photography was also of the utmost importance, providing an accurate way of recording the scene of a crime as well as a useful tool in the laboratory. In France, Alphonse Bertillon worked on a technique of contact photography to show up any erasures on documents. Bertillon, like many pioneers in the field of forensic science, was a generalist interested in many areas of criminal investigation. As well as applying photography to the detection process, he also made casts of tool marks at crime scenes for comparison with tools found in the possession of suspects, and he developed an identification system based on anatomical measurments and photographs.

Meanwhile, the concept of fingerprint identification was introduced and quickly became accepted across Europe (although the French police continued with Bertillon's system until after his death in 1914). Fingerprints provide a positive way of linking a particular suspect with a crime, and the method remains a mainstay of detection today, supported by vast numbers of recorded fingerprints – in the case of Scotland Yard, a computer database containing 4,000,000 sets of prints.

So from simple observation and trial-and-error techniques there gradually emerged the enormous body of knowledge and expertise that serves the twentieth-century forensic scientist. In the following chapters we will look in more detail at the work of the different departments, showing how the scene of a crime can be made to reveal its story.

Identifying points of similarity between a suspect's fingerprints and one of the millions now stored on police records.

CHAPTER TWO

The Scene of the Crime

The scene of a crime is the starting point for any forensic investigation, and success or failure in determining what happened depends on the information gathered there. A victim of crime, whether living or dead, is part of the scene, and must be examined with the same care as a room or a car -there may be vital clues on a victim's clothes or body.

The principle behind this painstaking search for evidence is simple, and was summed up by Dr. Edmond Locard of Lyon in the last century: every contact leaves a trace. Whenever two objects come into contact, there is a mutual transfer of material, no matter how slight. So whenever you open a door, your hand not only leaves fingerprints behind, but also picks up particles of dust or paint. And when two cars crash, they mark each other with traces of their different coloured paint, which can be matched visually and by chemical analysis. There is the same two-way transfer between the criminal and the scene, including the victim. In a struggle, for example, two people may unknowingly carry away traces of each other's hair, blood, saliva, and fibres from their clothes, any of which can be enough to prove that the contact took place.

The Integrity of the Scene

It is always important to maintain the integrity of the scene, which means nothing should be disturbed or removed until it is sent in a sealed, marked container to the laboratory, and nothing should be added, like the footprints of the police or bystanders. If anything can be shown to have altered the items found, they lose much of their value as evidence, which is why forensic investigators never touch anything with their bare hands until all tests are complete. It can be very difficult to sift

Lestrade showed us the exact spot at which the body had been found, and indeed, so moist was the ground, that I could plainly see the traces which had been left by the fall of the stricken man. To Holmes, as I could see by his eager face and peering eyes, very many other things were to be read upon the trampled grass.
(THE BOSCOMBE VALLEY MYSTERY)

The general procedure after the discovery of a dead body.

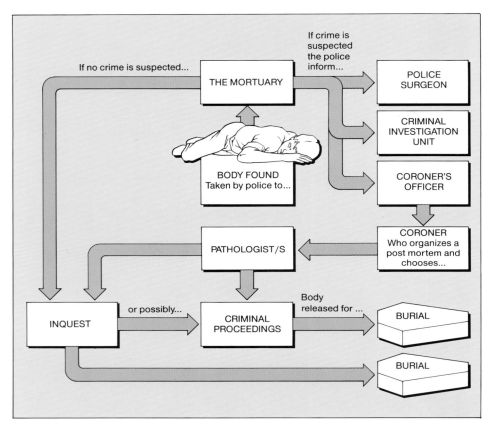

genuine evidence from additions to the scene, especially much later when items are looked at in isolation in the laboratory, away from the rest of the evidence which would set it in context. It is far better to avoid such problems from the start, and forensics experts often wear a full set of protective clothing when they examine the scene. This protection is both to keep the location free of contamination from those coming in, and to ensure the safety of the investigating officers -especially where blood or body fluids have been spilled, there is always the danger that it may carry hepatitis or the AIDS virus.

Collecting the Evidence

Photographs record the whole scene before anything is moved, to show general relationships between objects and close-up details. Then the collection process begins. The investigators will be looking for common types of evidence, like fingerprints, marks from shoes or tools, blood and fibres, but often surprising or apparently insignificant evidence provides an important clue. The half-burnt stub of a bookmatch was found at the scene of an arson attack, and was eventually shown to come from a book of matches found on the suspect. The arsonist could have been forgiven for doubting that a cardboard match would survive the fire, let alone help convict him afterwards, but another criminal left a far more obvious clue behind him. At the scene of a burglary, the investigators found the alarm bell out of action. The burglar had muffled the bell by tearing up some thin card and wedging it behind the clapper so that the bell would not ring. When the torn pieces were fitted together, they turned out to form the burglar's National Insurance card, complete with his individual identification number. Few criminals are so obliging in leaving hints to their identity.

A pathologist's sketch at the scene of the crime, with the pathologist's head and nose added at the bottom to show his vantage point.

'Painting' for Fingerprints

The trained eye is perhaps the scenes of crime investigator's most valuable tool, but recent developments in laser technology have resulted in a portable device which can reveal the invisible, especially fingerprints. Before, officers would dust for fingerprints in what they considered to be likely spots, like the areas around doors and windows, but this resulted in a great deal of wasted time, and probably meant that some prints in unlikely places were missed altogether. With the new portable laser, investigators can 'paint' any surface with laser light, showing up the location of any fingerprints, which can then be recorded in the usual way. This method is particularly useful for eliminating areas which look likely to contain prints, but which in fact show none; without the laser, they would have to be laboriously dusted bit by bit, just in case there was evidence to be found. The laser works by reacting with fluorescent material in the sweat in fingerprints, and possibly also with substances the finger may have touched, like oil. The result is a perfect, glowing fingerprint, visible to the naked eye.

However, high-tech methods like this are used mainly for more serious crimes, and for most minor crimes, like domestic robberies, the traditional techniques are quite sufficient.

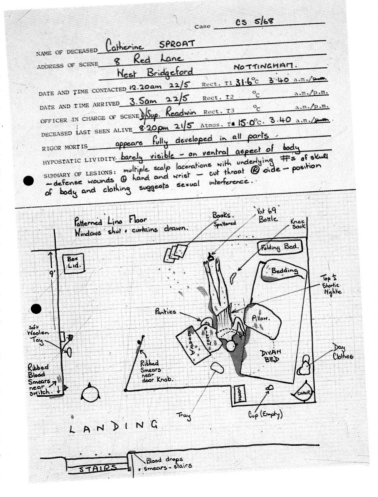

The suspect area is brushed all over with a fine powder – either aluminium powder or Bristol Black – and the powder sticks to the sweat in the finger mark. The impression is then literally 'lifted' off the surface with a low-adhesive sticky tape, and attached to a clear perspex sheet. This transparent sandwich is then photographed to provide a permanent, enlarged exhibit which can be studied and produced in court. (Fingerprints officers distinguish between the actual impression left at the scene, which they call a fingermark, and the recorded impression on paper, which is the fingerprint.)

The men involved in the Great Train Robbery of 1963 were convicted mainly on the evidence of fingerprints; little evidence was found at the scene of the crime on the train itself, but at Leatherslade Farm, their secret retreat, the men took less care and left fingermarks everywhere. Huge numbers of prints were recorded from the usual surfaces like doors and walls, and even from cutlery.

The Evidence of Blood

Methods of searching the scene of a murder in the 1940's.

Blood stains are another form of evidence which needs to be examined at the scene. If a lot of blood has been spilt, samples can be sent to the laboratory for tests

to determine the person's blood group and other biological information. Blood-stained clothes are usually sent as they are, sealed in a bag, and liquid blood will be collected in a clean glass container. But blood can do more than tell the blood group of the injured person: it can also tell investigators what sort of injury was sustained, and where the victim, assailant and witnesses were standing in relation to each other. The patterns made by blood spatters on walls, floors and clothing can help the investigator build up a detailed picture of what happened, and blood spattering evidence is often used to confirm or deny the story told by a suspect or witness.

London Metropolitan police divers preparing to search the Thames.

Analysing Blood Spatters

If the stain shows a bubbled, frothy effect it indicates coughed blood from damaged lungs; such marks show up best on non-absorbent surfaces like paint and glass, rather than fabric. Large stains are typical of bleeding from an artery; the marks will be fairly constant in size, and may cover quite a distance, as the pumping action of the heart makes blood spurt out of the damaged artery at a high pressure. In contrast, blood from a cut vein forms runs and drips, because there is little pressure behind it.

A puzzling pattern of blood was found at the scene of a death, where a man's body was found in his bedroom. The wallpaper and bedclothes were covered with blood, as was the man's face, but there was no sign of any injury on the body. The pattern of the stains strongly suggested arterial bleeding, but the investigators at the scene could find no explanation for this characteristic spattering. They were proved right by the post mortem, however, when a small object was found embedded in the man's ear; this turned out to be a matchstick, which the man had pushed into his ear, puncturing an artery in the ear. This tiny injury caused a jet of blood from his ear and the man, who was drunk at the time, bled to death.

In that case there were no suspicious circumstances, but in an American case the pattern of blood was used to tell whether a shooting case was a matter of self-defence or murder. A young woman was found dead with spattered blood on the wall and floor around her head – she had been shot, the bullet striking the bridge of her nose. The defendant claimed that he and the victim had been arguing, when she pointed a gun at him, so he shot her as she stood in front of him. But the victim was 152.5cm tall, while the blood stain only reached 75cm up the wall. The drops of blood formed a 'halo' on the wall around her head, showing that the impact of the bullet had made her head snap sharply backwards. The only way this low 'halo' of blood could have been formed was if the victim had been lying down when shot, either leaning on her elbows or lying on her back. So the defendant was shown to be lying, and a plea of self-defence was not possible.

The body being removed from the scene.

Laboratory Reconstructions

Sometimes a scene needs such careful examination that large parts of it are taken away and reconstructed at the forensic science laboratory. During the search for a mass-murderer in North London, the kitchen, lounge and part of the drainage system from a suspect's house were recreated in the laboratory; the wallpaper was removed without damaging it, and re-hung. The man was suspected of killing his victims in the kitchen, then disposing of parts of the bodies by flushing them down the drains. Because splashes of blood are so important in telling how and where an attack took place, the scientists recreated the rooms so they could look at individual blood spots in relation to the whole scene; in this way the sequence of events was reconstructed accurately.

Such large-scale reconstructions of houses are rare, however; it is more common for a whole car or van to be taken away for detailed examination by scientists. In the laboratory, many special techniques can be applied to a vehicle, including the use of lasers and other light sources to look for fingermarks and staining from body fluids. Once the vehicle is impounded, the investigators can be sure that no evidence is being lost or added to by the effects of weather or further use.

Preserving the integrity of the scene outdoors.

Collecting Evidence Outdoors

When a crime takes place in a open space, the forensic officer is faced with even more problems than at an indoor scene. Changes in the weather may alter or obliterate fragile pieces of evidence, and so speed is of the essence in gathering information. Rain may wash away traces like footmarks, but a fine day may mean that marks made in dew quickly dry and disappear, while even a light wind may blow away cigarette ash or loose hairs. There is no such thing as good weather for the investigator dealing with an outdoor scene. It is possible to cover the area with a 'scene tent', but even so it is hard to seal off a patch of woodland or a stretch of road in the same way as a house or a car. In such a case, forensics experts have to work particularly carefully to retrieve evidence in the pristine condition necessary if it is to be used in a court case.

The method of removing evidence follows several stages, beginning with the photographing of the whole scene, to record it as it was when the incident happened. Then a route is followed towards the centre of the scene, usually the route taken by the perpetrator; this is methodically cleared of anything that might be useful as evidence. At this stage a decision is made as to the relative importance of fingerprints and physical evidence, and priority will be given to one or the other. If, for example, a body needs to be moved for a post mortem examination, this will be done before fingerprints officers search the scene. But in many cases like robberies, fingerprints will be taken before other evidence is disturbed, because they are so easily obliterated.

Any item which investigators consider might be relevant is documented and sealed in a suitable container before being removed. Each piece of evidence is fully dealt with before moving on to the next, so the risks of confusion and contamination are minimised. Casts are made of tool marks on any surfaces which cannot be moved, and if a bullet is embedded in wood or plaster, a section of the surrounding material will be cut away. A spent bullet will bear markings made by the firing of the gun; if it is roughly prised free of its surroundings these marks may be damaged, and it may not be possible to match the bullet with a particular weapon.

There have been many cases in which criminals have been identified from bite marks found at the scene – sometimes these are on the body of the victim, but bite marks have also been found on hard foods like apples and cheese. In such cases, the marks must be reproduced quickly by taking photographs and casts, before dehydration distorts the impression.

Whether the scene is inside or out, simple or complicated, it is the source of all the evidence which forensic scientists will use to determine what happened. Modern methods of detection and collection are not very different from many of those used by Sherlock Holmes, except that increased sensitivity of testing techniques means that ever smaller traces of evidence can be discovered and analysed, and so the prevention of contamination is more important than ever.

A police photographer recording the precise points of impact in a car crash.

CHAPTER THREE

The Investigation of Fire

They had spent the morning raking among the ashes of the burned wood-pile and besides the charred organic remains they had secured several discoloured metal discs. I examined them with care, and there was no doubt that they were trouser buttons.
(THE NORWOOD BUILDER)

Fire investigation is one of the busiest branches of forensic science, dealing with all fatal fires, cases where arson is suspected, and all sorts of explosions, from the accidental gas leak to terrorist bombs. The study of fire science includes building design and a knowledge of the flammable qualities of furniture, as well as an understanding of the chemistry of fire and the dynamics of how it spreads.

On the face of it, fire destroys evidence, and many people try to cover up other crimes by setting fire to the scene, but in fact a great deal of information can be gleaned from the remains of a fire. And these days, fire investigation has gone beyond merely sifting through the debris for obvious clues like bones and buttons, as in the Sherlock Holmes story above. The modern fire scientist can call upon a battery of sophisticated tests, as well as a detailed understanding of the mechanics of fire – how it starts, and how it spreads.

The circumstances surrounding a fire can provide as much information as an analysis of what is left afterwards. Finding out what activities went on at the scene can suggest what to look for in the ashes, and can help point up anything suspicious. For example, traces of petrol found in a burned garage are to be expected, but the same traces in a burned grocery need explaining.

Finding the 'Seat' of the Fire

Fire investigators are looking for the answers to three main questions: where, how, and when did the fire start ? The place where a fire started is called the 'seat', and is usually where there are the most intense signs of burning – if there are two such sites, with no possible connection, then arson is strongly indicated. Fire scientists can tell how a fire started – because of an electrical fault or a dropped cigarette, for instance – by laboratory tests as well as by assessing whether it was a flaming or a smouldering fire. Generally, a naked flame will cause a flaming

A typical domestic fire caused by a fallen cigarette into an armchair.

fire, while a smouldering object like a lit cigarette or charcoal from a barbecue will cause a smouldering fire. Investigating if a fire was of electrical origin ranges from the apparently obvious, like checking if the building is in fact connected to the electricity supplies, to the complex, like tracing the wiring and fuses to search for signs of arcing or power overload. (It is surprisingly common for people to claim an electrical fault is the cause of fire, when there is no power supply to the point where the blaze obviously started.) If a particular heater or kettle is suspected as the cause, the scientists may test an identical, undamaged device in the laboratory, deliberately overloading it to see if a fire can be provoked. The time of a blaze can be estimated by working out how long the objects at the scene would have sustained a fire.

The Mystery of 'Spontaneous Combustion'

Different types of furniture burn in different ways, so the same cause can produce a variety of results. Modern furniture filled with polyurethane foam ignites very quickly into a flaming fire, so that a match dropped onto a foam-filled chair may turn the room into an inferno in only three to four minutes. Often all the stuffing and covers are burnt but the wooden frame remains more or less intact, only charred on the outside; this is because such a fire flares up fast but quickly consumes the easily-flammable foam, and then dies down before the wooden frame can ignite properly.

Older types of furniture, especially when not ignited by a naked flame, tend to smoulder without bursting into flames – which is less spectacular but may have

25

An example of apparent 'spontaneous combustion': very localised smouldering which burns the body but leaves the rest of the room untouched.

equally destructive results. In one case, an old lady knocked over an electric heater while sitting in her armchair. The heater lay against the chair, which was stuffed with horsehair, and it began to smoulder. Because the door and windows were closed, there was a limited supply of oxygen in the room, further impeding the outbreak of a flaming fire. The smouldering went on for many hours until the chair, and the carpet and floorboards under it, were completely destroyed, and the old lady was dead. But her body was not burned as such; she died relatively quickly form the effects of thick smoke from the horsehair, and her body was only charred where it was touching the chair. The rest of the room, too, was undamaged by the very localised combustion of the chair, and even the carpet a few feet from the fire was not burnt.

This very contained sort of smouldering fire provides a possible explanation for reported cases of 'spontaneous combustion', where people are supposed to burst into flames for no reason, and burn fiercely without damaging their immediate surroundings. 'Spontaneous combustion' is never witnessed, and it easy to see how some cases could appear inexplicable without a detailed understanding of how different sorts of fire work, especially if the body is almost totally destroyed.

The Deliberate Fire

Because fire is a destructive process, it is often started deliberately in an attempt to cover up another crime, especially a killing. It is hoped that the scene of a crime or a body will be so badly damaged that no evidence will remain, but this is seldom the case. Simple things like the location of broken window glass may yield damning information − tiny fragments of glass inside the scene of a fire show that the window was broken before the blaze started, so it was probably started by an intruder rather than by an electrical fault or a cooking accident inside the house. Police scenes of crime officers and members of the fire service are trained to preserve all possible evidence, and to cause minimal damage in putting out a fire, so such clues are often discovered.

Usually, the presence of flammable liquids is detectable, even in minute quantities; substances used to start a fire and increase its intensity are called accelerants, and samples are routinely taken from areas where an accelerant might have been used. An arsonist might think that all traces of an accelerant like petrol or methylated spirits will be burned away, but various clues will point a fire investigator in the right direction. Sometimes the smell of an accelerant will linger to rouse suspicion, or else the pattern of burning may not be consistent with a normal flaming fire; at the scene, the nose and eyes of a trained investigator can be sensitive tools of detection.

Testing for 'Accelerants'

Samples are taken from the surface of the floor, if it is absorbent like wood or carpet, or from under floorboards and tiles, where liquids like petrol will seep in the seconds before ignition. Even traces of evaporated petrol and other hydrocarbons can be detected with up-to-date facilities in the forensic laboratory. Such samples are analysed by gas chromatography, which can tell the identity and quantity of individual chemical compounds in a substance. In this test, the sample is vaporised and passed through a column whose contents slow down the separate chemical components of the sample by different amounts. The separated compounds emerge from the column one by one into a detector, which produces a graph showing different peaks for each compound. The location of each peak along a scale shows the compound's identity, while the height of the peak show the quantity present. In this way, even tiny traces of volatile substances like petrol can be identified and measured with amazing accuracy.

A door which has been fire-bombed through the letter-box.

Fire investigators can call on other high-tech devices in uncovering the secrets of fire. With an electron microscope they can examine tiny traces of evidence at enormous magnification, and with X-ray equipment the can see what lies beneath the surface of larger articles. X-rays, for example, are often used to look inside a fuse in search of a fault which could have caused a spark, or over-heating. In cases of deliberate fires, the arsonist often tries to put the blame on an electrical fault, but this can be ruled out by proving no such fault existed.

The Arson that Backfired

Quite apart from the possibility that covering up another crime by fire may leave as many clues as the original incident, the arsonist can suffer a more immediate fate; playing with fire can be a dangerous business, as one man found to his cost. In South-East London a few years ago, a man killed his wife with an axe and, perhaps hoping to make the death look like an accident, he attempted to set fire to her hairdressing salon. He

Smoke in the trachea shows clearly at the post mortem that the victim died inhaling fumes at the scene of the fire, and was not placed there dead, beforehand.

A finger from an electrocuted body, showing the point of contact with the current.

doused the body and the salon with petrol, and lit the liquid – what he did not know was that, given time to evaporate, petrol fumes produce an explosive mixture with air. When the man lit the liquid petrol, this dangerous mixture in the air also ignited, causing an explosion which blew out the front of the shop. The man was caught in the blast and subsequent fire, and died at the scene of his crime. Fire investigators found enough evidence to piece together this sorry chain of events, but of course they could not tell whether the man died accidentally while trying to disguise the murder of his wife, or whether he really intended to kill himself in the fire, and succeeded more quickly than he hoped.

Bombs and Explosions

Forensic fire investigators are called to deal with all sorts of explosions, not just arson attempts that have gone wrong. In many ways, explosions are more satisfying to examine from a forensic point of view that ordinary fires, because it is very rare not to reach a definite answer about the cause. The majority of cases dealt with by forensics experts are not headline-grabbing bombs, but are caused by gas or petrol, and as we have already seen, the presence of flammable liquids like petrol can often be detected at the scene. Gas explosions are the most obvious in cause, for even if the gas itself has all dispersed, it must have reached the scene somehow, either along the mains gas supply, or in a portable gas cylinder feeding an individual appliance. When gas explodes it produces what is called a dispersed explosion, with a general 'pushing' effect over a wide range. By contrast, a substance like gelignite will cause a condensed explosion, which is more violent and more localised. It often produces a crater, but does not affect such a wide area.

As well as causing different effects, explosives used in bombs leave traces which can be identified by chemical and visual techniques. Swabs taken from a scene can reveal the chemicals which caused the blast, while the container and detonator of a bomb will be blown into tiny tell-tale fragments. On 12th October 1984, the Grand Hotel in Brighton was bombed by the IRA. during the Conservative party conference, in an attempt to kill Mrs. Thatcher, the then Prime Minister. The blast missed its main target, but killed and injured other guests at the hotel. One woman's body was found to carry flash burns, and forensic scientists realised she must have been near the centre of the explosion. Various fragments from a cast iron bath and pieces of masonry were recovered from her body before a tiny unidentified particle was found: it was only the size of a pinhead. This tiny speck was scrutinised by scientists at the Metropolitan Police Forensic Science Laboratory; using an electron microscope to magnify it 100,000 times, its fused surface was examined. Then an X-ray spectrometer identified the individual components of the fragment, a sandwich of copper, nickel and gold backed by glass fibre resin – part of an electrical circuit board of a type used in almost all home computers. This minuscule piece of evidence is most important, because it tells scientists how the bomb was timed; a device with an electronic timer using this sort of circuitry could have been planted up to six months before the bombing, primed to explode at a particular moment. So the most insignificant item can prove to be vital in piecing together the jigsaw of past events.

Combing for clues through the still smouldering debris at a warehouse.

Forensic science covers many areas of expertise, and in most instances an investigation will draw on the skills of various departments when trying to reconstruct a true picture of what has happened. The following case is an example of such a joint operation; it began with the investigation of a burning van, and soon involved experts in the fields of fire, pathology, biology and ballistics.

Combining Forensic Expertise

In 1985 a farmer was working in one of his fields on the north bank of the Thames in Essex, when he saw a van pull up. Fearing that the van was being used to dump rubbish on his land, the farmer was approaching the van when it suddenly erupted into flames. At the same time, he saw an old brown motorcycle being ridden away. When the police reached the scene, they found the body of a man in the back of the burned van, and at once called in Dr. Kevin Dunnicliffe, a forensic scientist specialising in fire investigation. Dr. Dunnicliffe examined the body and vehicle, and was alerted by the smell of petrol – the fire had been no accident, but was an attempt to destroy the body. In the mortuary, a post mortem confirmed his suspicions, as four shotgun wounds were found in the dead man's back. It was at this point that the inquiry broadened out, and the findings of other forensic scientists became invaluable.

Wadding material was taken from the shotgun wounds and passed to the ballistics department, who identified it as coming from a distinctive type of cartridge case last made in 1959. Meanwhile, police inquiries led them to a garage some 30 miles away in Colchester, where they found an old brown motorcycle like that seen by the farmer. The dead man also had links with the garage, and this was enough to bring a team of forensic scientists to investigate. Dr. Dunnicliffe took with him a ballistics expert to look at any firearms evidence, and a biologist to deal with

Tracing the 'seat' of a fire in a theatre back to an electrical fault.

The silhouette of a body removed from a smoke-blackened room.

bloodstains. The garage had obviously been cleaned recently, but despite this the team found two important pieces of evidence. The first was a bloodstain, which was not only identified as human, but also proved to be of the same blood group as the dead man. The second piece of evidence was a shotgun cartridge case of the type which had killed the victim – and this case also bore characteristic markings showing it had been fired from a Browning semi-automatic shotgun. So the scientists had discovered the scene of the shooting, and the type of gun used.

Acting on information, the police now raided a suspect's house, and there they found the same sort of cartridges, along with a rifle. This was not the weapon they were looking for, but from their records they discovered it had been stolen from a farmhouse three years before – along with a Browning semi-automatic shotgun. A pair of the suspect's shoes also matched a mark found at the garage, and despite being cleaned, they still bore traces of blood. So a link had been proved between the suspect, the shooting at the garage, and the dumping of the blazing van. However, a remarkable example of detective work and sheer good luck was to provide a final, damning piece of evidence.

When the burning van was first found, the police had asked for information about the brown motorcycle. Now a man came forward to say that he had nearly collided with such a motorcycle near the scene, and as it swerved to avoid his car, a piece of cloth had fallen from it onto his vehicle. The witness had driven on to his workplace, where the piece of cloth was used as a rag to clean machinery before eventually being thrown away. Of course, the rubbish had been routinely collected and taken to the local refuse tip. The police began the unpleasant task of combing the rubbish tip and finally, after a long and messy search, the cloth was recovered. Forensic scientists found that the cloth perfectly matched the torn edge of a blanket found in the suspect's home, conclusively tying the man to the crime.

CHAPTER FOUR

Firearms and the Science of Ballistics

It is a sad fact that as gun ownership increases, so does the workload of forensics experts concerned with ballistics. Fortunately, society is not quite as violent as our fears sometimes make it seem, and a good deal of the work done at firearms laboratories does not involve violent crime like armed robbery, but cases of illegal possession and accidents. (There is no doubt that in some countries where gun ownership is legalised, such as in the United States, the incidence of violent crimes involving firearms is far higher than in Britain.)

When more serious matters are dealt with by the police, such as fatal shootings and acts of terrorism, it is these cases which provide the greatest scope for the forensic scientist. The firearms expert can be called upon to provide the answers to many questions: what type of weapon was used; the range and direction of the shot; whether a suspect gun could have made such a shot; and if a bullet came from a specific gun. It is common knowledge that every person's fingerprints are unique, but less widely known that every single gun can be identified by equally individual markings.

No-one had heard a shot. And yet there was the dead man, and there the revolver bullet, which had mushroomed out, as soft-nosed bullets will, and so inflicted a wound which must have caused instantaneous death.
(THE EMPTY HOUSE)

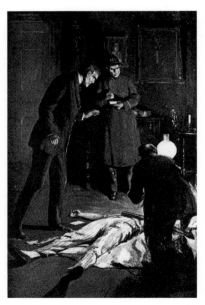

Identifying a Gun by 'Rifling'

When a self-loading pistol is fired, the bullet is discharged, and the cartridge case is usually ejected to make room for the next cartridge. If recovered, these items can identify the exact gun used, not just point to the right make and model. As the bullet travels down the barrel of the gun, grooves within the barrel make it spin to increase the accuracy of its flight, and this leaves a pattern of fine scratches on the spent bullet. These scratches are known as 'rifling', and thanks to tiny, random imperfections within the grooves inside the barrel, the scratches on each bullet are unique to the gun that fired it. The major rifling marks may be similar in another gun of the same type, but minuscule faults in the manufacturing process and later cleaning will add extra scratches which are individual to each gun. Rifling marks on a spent bullet therefore form a sort of 'fingerprint' of the gun which fired it. Similarly,

31

the cartridge case is marked by various actions within the gun, particularly the impact of the firing pin. The surface of the firing pin bears unique faults due to corrosion, and again it leaves a random pattern on the discarded cartridge case. Depending on the type of gun, the case may also be marked by the extractor claw and the ejector port as it leaves the gun.

A 12 bore shotgun on a comparison microscope TV monitor showing a split image of the 'headstamp' on a cartridge.

Identifying Bullets

These individual patterns are supplemented by the more major marks, which reveal the make and model of the weapon even to the naked eye of the ballistics expert. On a cartridge case, for example, this may be shown by the angle between the marks of the extractor claw and the ejector. With a bullet, the information is contained within the main rifling marks: the number of grooves, and the direction of spin. Different gun makers use different designs, and at the firearms laboratory there will be a huge reference collection of guns and ammunition going back many years – in the Home Office National Firearms Laboratory at Huntingdon, England, they have collected about a million rounds of assorted ammunition. The scientists compare the markings by firing some of these reference bullets from the suspect weapon, then checking the resulting marks with those on bullets recovered from the body of a victim, or the scene.

An X-ray showing the dispersal of shot in the body from a range of 1–2 metres.

This checking procedure is made relatively simple by a comparison microscope; two microscopes are linked by an optical bridge, so that both specimens can be seen at once in the same eyepiece or on a screen. In this way, the fine scratches and grooves on a test bullet can be lined up with those on any found at the scene to show if they match. This explains why such care is exercised in removing bullets from the scene of a shooting, for if any scratches are obliterated, or new ones added, a possible match will be obscured.

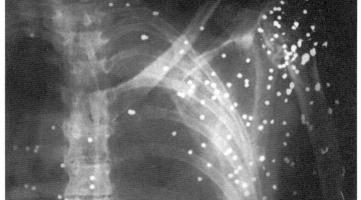

The Trail of the Canadian .38

The skill and experience of ballistics experts in applying these identification techniques led to the discovery of a murder which at first appeared to be an accident. When the police were called to an antiques warehouse, they found the body of a woman with a severe head injury, which was attributed to an accidental fall. There were a few suspicious points, however, so the pathologist was asked to perform a particularly careful post mortem examination of the body – and this revealed what looked like a bullet entry wound in her head, but no exit wound. The head of the Home Office National Firearms Laboratory examined an X-ray of the head and concluded that an opaque object on the film appeared to be a deformed .38 calibre bullet embedded in the woman's brain. The bullet was removed and washed, and just by looking at it without any special equipment, the ballistics expert was able to tentatively identify it as a .38 bullet brought from Canada during the Second World War, which had been fired from a Smith & Wesson revolver.

Now the investigation moved to the dead woman's home. Her husband said that there were signs of an armed robbery at the antiques warehouse: a large sum of money and some jewellery were missing from an opened safe there, and he thought his wife must have been killed during the course of the robbery. He gave the police descriptions of two men he had seen acting suspiciously in a car near the warehouse, and the police circulated this information. However, at the house, it was found that the husband was illegally in possession of two handguns. Neither of these was the Smith & Wesson revolver the police were looking for, but their presence made the ballistics expert suspicious, especially as both were loaded and ready to fire. A detailed search of the man's gun room ensued, where plenty of legally-owned guns and ammunition were found, including some bullets of the right calibre, but the wrong make and date. Finally, in the gun safe, the ballistics expert found six rounds of .38 ammunition, hidden among boxed piles of .22 ammunition, with the marking DC 43 – Dominion Cartridge 1943, a Canadian brand from the second World War. The discovery prompted the police to take the gun room apart, until they located a secret safe under the floor. In it was a Smith & Wesson revolver. He opened the cylinder, and saw five live rounds of ammunition – and one spent cartridge case. This must be the murder weapon.

But the forensic scientist does not rely merely on such presumptive evidence, and firing tests were carried out back at the laboratory. That same evening, these tests conclusively identified the fatal bullet as coming from the husband's hidden gun, and he was charged with the murder of his wife. At the trial, he did not deny that his gun had fired the killing shot, but tried to suggest that the gun had gone off accidentally during a scuffle with his wife. The ballistics expert was able to show the jury that mechanical faults on the gun in fact made it less prone to accidental discharge than other guns of the same type. The man was found guilty of the murder of his wife, and sentenced accordingly.

The Canadian .38 bullet under a comparison microscope.

Comparing 2 unfired 12 bore cartridges for operational marking to see if they have been through the mechanism of a pump action gun.

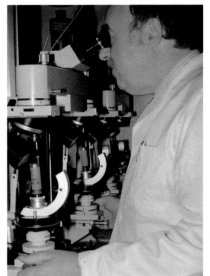

Reconstructing the Behaviour of Bullets

There are various facilities for test-firing weapons, including large outdoor firing ranges bristling with equipment, bullet recovery containers, and indoor ranges fitted with detectors which can tell the speed of a flying bullet. As its name suggests, the bullet recovery container is where test shots of suspect weapons are made, so the spent bullet can be retrieved and the markings analysed. Discharged bullets have to be slowed down and caught without damage. The equipment for this is remarkably simple, ranging from a box stuffed with cotton wadding to a long cylindrical tank full of water.

It is often necessary to reconstruct how a bullet would have behaved over various distances and conditions, to tell whether it could have been used in a certain offence. The speed of a fired bullet can be measured by computer-aided optical equipment. In a room at the Home Office laboratory at Huntingdon, two detectors look up at the lights overhead, which emit infra-red radiation. As a bullet passes above the first detector, it briefly blots out the infra-red signal being received, and the same thing happens a fraction of a second later as it passes over the second detector. A quartz time system in the computer measures the delay between these two interruptions of the infra-red signal, and produces a read-out of the bullet's velocity. This equipment can be used for air guns which fire pellets at a few hundred feet per second, right up to high-power rifle ammunition which can travel at four thousand feet per second. Other detectors in the outdoor ranges interpret the flight path and impact energy of a bullet even over a very long range. In this way, ballistics experts do not just estimate the course of events at a shooting incident – they can state exactly what happened.

The small entry and spread exit point of a shotgun wound.

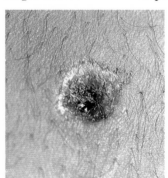
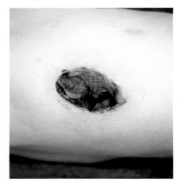

Bullet Wounds

Another aspect of the firearm examiner's work is the interpretation of bullet wounds and the marks caused by discharge material when a gun is fired. Close to the muzzle, the high temperature gases can burn or blacken the skin and clothing of the victim.

High-speed photography shows that a bullet is not the only thing to leave the barrel of a gun. When the film is frozen with the bullet 30cm from the barrel, a cloud of tiny white spots is seen surrounding it. These are unburned particles of nitro-cellulose powder, forced down the barrel and travelling at supersonic speed. Despite this speed, their flight will stop within a few metres; but if the gun is fired near its target, this powder leaves a sort of tattoo pattern in flesh or fabric, which can help determine how far away the shot was fired. Each particle of nitro-cellulose also contains traces of lead and barium, which come from the primer. These traces can be chemically detached using paper pressing from the clothes or skin of a victim to help determine the range of a shot even more closely, up to a distance of 2 metres. After examination on the scanning electron microscope, these traces can confirm the distance of the suspect from the firearm. (Because these particles travel some distance from the gun, their presence on the clothes or hands of a suspect does not prove that he actually fired the shot.)

A scientist using an endoprobe – a fibre optic probe – to examine the bore of an UZI sub-machine gun.

When a gun is fired with the barrel touching the victim, there will be severe blackening and burning round the wound, and the clothes and skin may be ripped in a star-shaped pattern: this caused by high-pressure gases being forced into the target, then ripping outwards to escape. This pattern of wounding is typical of a suicidal shot, but could also be produced if someone else pressed the gun against the victim's body.

An ingeniously homemade gun recovered by the police.

As the range increases to about 10cm, the blackened area around the wound increases in diameter but is not so intense, showing that the burning elements in the shot have had time to spread out a little. Once the range is increased beyond 20cm, there is very little blackening, but the nitro-cellulose particles will be embedded in the target like tiny shotgun pellets, leaving a permanent 'tattoo' record in the clothing and skin of a victim. All tests are conducted with the suspect weapon and identical ammunition, as great variations in blackening and powder effects can be produced by different cartridges, and the results are compared with actual wounds and marks. This gives a very accurate determination of how far away the gun was fired. Such detailed information is important because when firearms cases come to court, the defence often claims that the injury was caused by a suicide attempt or the accidental discharge of a gun during a fall or a fight – so if the shot was shown to have been fired from quite a distance, such a defence breaks down.

For instance, if the pattern of wounding indicates a range of 70cm, it rules out the possibility of a self-inflicted injury, whether suicidal or accidental, because no-one could possibly hold a gun that far away from their body. Of course, the expertise of the forensic scientist often helps to clear suspects, too, by showing that apparently suspicious circumstances have an innocent explanation.

Death in a Tractor

One such case occurred on a farm, where a farmer was rolling peas in his tractor. He was later found dead with a head injury inside the tractor cab, and his shotgun was found lying some distance away in the field. It seemed as though an unknown person had shot the farmer, then fled, dropping the gun during his escape. The affair was treated from the start as a murder inquiry, and the forensic science laboratory's ballistics department was called in. The gun in question was found to be quite old, with exposed hammers, and the left lock was seriously defective. It was also discovered that the farmer usually kept the shotgun in his tractor cab, and on the basis of their findings the forensic scientists reconstructed the incident as follows. The farmer must have reached for his gun while the tractor was still moving, probably to shoot some vermin he had seen, when the weapon slipped from his hands and fell out of the open door. As it fell, the back of the exposed hammer hit one of the metal steps up to the cab, and because of this defect, the gun fired in the farmer's face. The recoil energy from the shot then threw the gun away from the vehicle, while the tractor continued rolling on for a while before stalling. Without the experience and knowledge of the firearms examiners this mysterious-looking case would have perplexed the police, who might still have been hunting a non-existent murderer to this day.

The spread of a shotgun wound relative to distance, showing a split wound with blackening around the edges from close range contact on the bone.

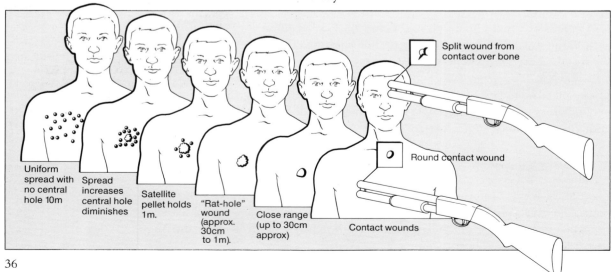

Uniform spread with no central hole 10m

Spread increases central hole diminishes

Satellite pellet holds 1m.

"Rat-hole" wound (approx. 30cm to 1m).

Close range (up to 30cm approx)

Contact wounds

Split wound from contact over bone

Round contact wound

CHAPTER FIVE

Dentistry:
The 'Fingerprint'
of the Mouth

As we have seen, dental evidence has been used for recognition purposes for many hundreds of years, and in this century dental records have famously helped to identify the badly-burned corpses of Adolf Hitler and Eva Braun, found in Hitler's bunker. The principle behind forensic dentistry is that the various features of the mouth show a vast range of individual characteristics, which do not change throughout life. The combination of these personal characteristics is different in everybody, making positive identification possible. Some such features, like the cracks and wrinkles in the lips which can produce prints, do not last long after death, but artificial dentures and the teeth themselves will survive fire, water and burial. One of the major modern uses of forensic dentistry is the identification of disfigured bodies in cases of mass disaster, like air and rail crashes.

In 1944, the Barnum & Bailey Circus tent burned down in America, and of 268 victims of the fire, 162 were identified by means of their dental records. As well as showing the identity of unknown corpses, forensic dentists are involved in evaluating assault injuries and child abuse; they also interpret bite marks found in food at the scene of a crime, and on victims' bodies.

Routine x-ray photographs taken during life provide a particularly useful form of recognition, because they give objective information about a person's teeth and mouth which can be compared with x-rays taken after death. Most people will have some x-rays in their dental records, and these show details not visible in the mouth, like unfilled cavities, unerupted teeth which have not yet appeared, and previous damage. If there are no x-rays for comparison, forensic dentists examine the teeth of a corpse as they would a living person, checking their findings against any written records or charts made before death.

It was the body of a tall, well-made man, about forty years of age. He lay upon his back, his face upturned, with his white teeth grinning through his short, black beard.

(THE ABBEY GRANGE)

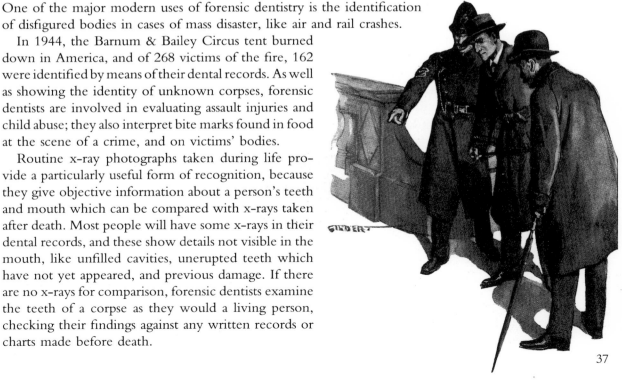

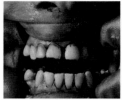

An apple with bite marks found at the scene of a murder could have been bitten by the victim or the murderer: the forensic specialist matched the teeth of the corpse to the apple.

Bite marks on a baby's body show up under ultra-violet light.

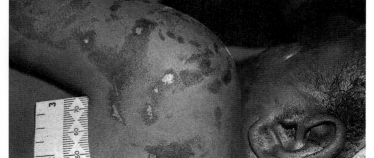

Dentures

Another very accurate method of identification is to look at any dentures worn by the deceased; the cases of Dr. Joseph Warren in 1775 and the Countess of Salisbury in 1835 show that evidence from dentures has been used in this way for many years. These days, false teeth are made very precisely to fit each person's mouth, and this careful construction makes it easy to conclusively identify the wearer. Dentures are also extremely tough, and are even resistant to acid, as John George Haigh (the Chelsea 'acid bath murderer') found to his cost.

In 1949, Mrs. Durand-Deacon was reported missing, and police suspicions fell on Haigh. In his possession they found a large tub of sulphuric acid. From the black sludge at the bottom of this container a few fragments of bone were recovered – along with a full set of dentures. These were identified by a dentist as those he had made for Mrs. Durand-Deacon; he even recognised repairs he had made to the false teeth over the years. Haigh is on record as believing that murder could not be proved without the presence of a body, but the survival of Mrs. Durand-Deacon's dentures ensured that her killer was convicted of the murder.

Sometimes, however, no records exist of any dental work carried out before death, and as a last resort the forensic dentist may turn to ordinary family photographs for identification. This is a rather unsatisfactory method because it relies on the dentist's subjective interpretation of the picture, but it can provide enough information to make an identification possible. For example, the skeleton of a woman was found in a shallow grave under some ferns at Salwick near Blackpool in England. The police suspected it was the remains of a missing woman, Mrs. Dorothy Harding, and they tried to trace her dental records, but although she was known to have had two teeth extracted and eight filled about three years before her death, the records were never found. Finally the photographic department of the Lancashire Constabulary superimposed a picture of the skull and teeth over a photograph taken at the woman's wedding. There were twenty-three points which compared well between the two pictures, and so the body was identified as that of Mrs. Harding. It is particularly poignant that because people are usually smiling broadly, wedding photographs are useful for this sort of comparison.

The Identikit Picture from Teeth

Teeth can tell the forensic dentist a great deal about the person they come from, including the age, sex, and sometimes even the race of an unidentified corpse.

 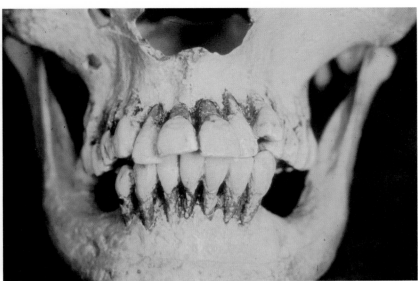

Age can be estimated from facts like the number of teeth fully erupted into the mouth, the presence of wisdom teeth or signs of their extraction, and worn-down tooth surfaces. The difference between the sexes is shown by the relative sizes of the teeth: in the male, they are usually larger than in the female, especially the canine in the lower jaw. Even just measuring the width of this tooth provides an accurate determination of sex in about three quarters of cases. There is also a method of telling sex from the dental pulp cells within the tooth. This hard tissue is broken down and stained with a chemical dye which makes certain structures in the cell nucleus fluoresce under a special light source. Women have two X chromosomes in each of their cells, but men have an X and a Y chromosome, and it is the Y chromosome which is fluorescent in this test. (The same technique can also be applied to cells from hair, saliva and blood.)

The distinctive passport photograph smile of this victim was a vital clue to identifying the crooked upper incisor of her skull when it was found.

Racial Differences

Various dental characteristics occur in different racial groups; for instance, 95% of the American Indian and 91% of the Chinese populations have distinctive shovel-shaped incisor teeth. (Anthropologists use such information in studying the geographic origins of groups like the North and South American Indians, to find out when and how they arrived in the continent.) There are also geographical variations in the incidence of tooth decay, which can provide a helpful pointer towards nationality. Britons, Americans and Danes have far more decay and consequently more repairs than West Africans, Russians and certain Asians, probably due to differences in diet. Such natural differences are supplemented by variations in

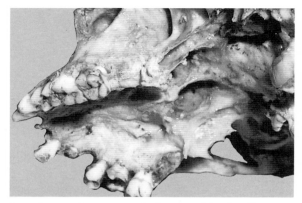

The decomposing upper jaw of a body recovered after three weeks exposure. Its identity was confirmed through dental records.
The biting surfaces of the cast below were marked, and matched exactly with the bite marks (right).

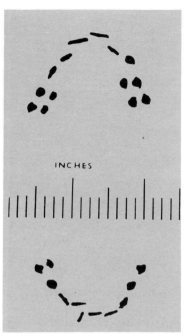

dental practice around the world. In Europe, crowns are often made from stainless steel or semi-precious metals, while in Latin America gold is commonly used. The information gained from such differences may seem tenuous and of minimal use in identification, but in a disaster like an air crash, where bodies of several nationalities are known to be present, it can prove extremely valuable.

Bite Marks

Perhaps the most fascinating aspect of forensic dentistry is identification by bite marks. Impressions left by a criminal's teeth in food or on the victim's body can be matched with the suspect, and these marks alone are often enough to prove guilt or innocence. In August 1967, thieves broke into a grocer's shop in a Scottish village, and during the raid one of the robbers bit into an apple, but did not finish eating it. When the apple was discovered, a plaster impression was quickly taken before it could dry out and distort the pattern of the teeth. Artificial teeth of the right shape and size were fitted in the individual depressions left by the thief's teeth. These artificial teeth were waxed together and lifted out, forming a perfect reconstruction of the man's dentistry. When two suspects were brought in by the police for questioning, one man's teeth

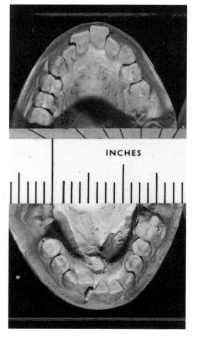

40

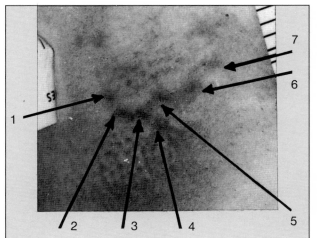 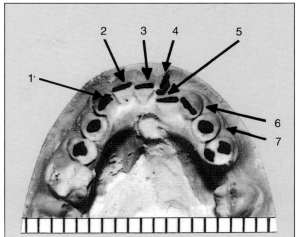

The cast of teeth from the suspect's mouth revealed an irregular tooth in the lower jaw, a 'pickle-chaser', (no. 4) which corresponded exactly to the bite wounds (left).

were so characteristic that he was immediately confronted with the dental evidence. Faced with this proof that he had been at the scene, the man at once confessed, and the pair were both found guilty of the offence. And the apple which caught them is still kept intact in formalin, with the bite mark still visible.

It is surprisingly common to find bite marks on the body of a victim, especially in cases of child abuse and sexual assault; despite the elasticity of the skin, these marks can often be precisely matched with the attacker. Another Scottish case demonstrates the useful details which can be gathered from bite marks on skin. On the night of 16th May 1973, the body of a woman was found in a house at Greenock in Scotland. She had been murdered, and her body was covered with extensive injuries, including some circular marks on the breasts and abdomen whose shape suggested they were bites. The body was photographed, then washed, and the presence of human bite marks was confirmed. There were several distinctive features to the teeth which had inflicted the bites: one of the upper incisors was slightly rotated in position, and the upper left canine had made a larger mark than the upper right one, suggesting that it was less pointed. The police had a suspect, and casts were made of his teeth for comparison – at this stage, the suspect tried to implicate another man in the crime, and casts were taken from his mouth as well. However, it was soon clear that the suspect's teeth matched all the distinctive characteristics of the bite mark, while the man he tried to blame had very unusual teeth which could not possibly have made the marks on the body. It was equally important from the forensic scientists's point of view that there were no features in the bite mark which would have excluded the suspect, making the case watertight. At the trial, the man at first pleaded not guilty, but when he heard the dental evidence, he immediately changed his plea to one of guilty.

CHAPTER SIX

Fingerprints:
The Unchanging Record

As he held the match nearer I saw that it was more than a stain. It was the well-marked print of a thumb.
'Look at that with your magnifying glass, Mr. Holmes.'
'Yes, I am doing so.'
'You are aware that no two thumb-marks are alike?'
'I have heard something of the kind.'
(THE NORWOOD BUILDER)

In the late nineteenth century, when Sherlock Holmes was solving his fictional cases, it was only just being realised that fingerprints had an important part to play in apprehending and identifying criminals. It was gradually discovered that everybody's fingerprints are unique and unchanging, and that invisible prints can be brought to light by various means and recorded for future reference. And although the usefulness of fingerprints in detection is now widely known, they are still among the most common types of evidence found at scenes of crime.

A thief or attacker acting on the spur of the moment may not think to cover his hands, and those committing a carefully planned offence may still find gloves an encumbrance, preferring to rely for protection on the fact that they have no criminal record, so the police do not know their prints. As we shall see, however, such confidence is often misplaced.

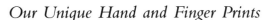

Our Unique Hand and Finger Prints

When we consider prints, we tend to think only of those made by the fingertips, but the palms of the hands and soles of the feet also have a distinctive pattern. All these areas of the body are characterised by small ridges in the skin, which stay the same throughout life. They are formed in the womb, when the foetus is about 21 weeks old, and they remain unchanged until some time after death, making the recognition of corpses possible. It has been known for people to try to alter or obliterate their prints by cutting their fingertips, or burning the skin with acid, but such attempts are usually in vain. Minor skin damage is easily repaired by the body, so that the same ridges reappear in the new skin; and even if major scarring results, the rest of the hand will still leave the same prints, while the scars themselves form a new identifying mark.

Although many people's fingerprints form similar patterns, the details are unique; even identical twins have different

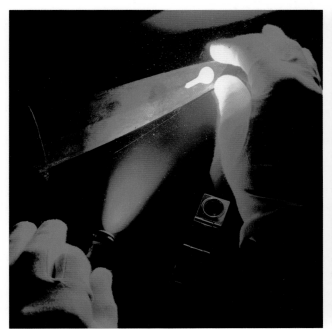 

fingerprints. The general patterns form loops, arches, whorls, and composites of these types, but the fingerprints officer will be looking within the general design of lines for details like broken ridges and bifurcations (points where the lines divide). Nobody has the same 'coincidence sequence' of these tiny characteristics, so the fingerprints expert will try to find a sufficient number of the same details in the same order to make an identification. Because the skin is elastic, the distances between features are not measured; but the various characteristics remain constant in relation to each other, so the ridges between different features are counted to build up a 'map' of the complex pattern.

'Lifting' Prints

Fingerprints are formed when the sweat and oils produced by the skin are deposited on a surface. On a hard, non-porous object, the fingermark stands slightly proud of the surface, and after it has been brushed with powder to make it visible, the whole print is physically removed from the surface with low-adhesive tape. When fingerprints officers speak of 'lifting' prints, this is precisely what they do. Unfortunately, many rough surface will not hold prints, and other smooth items like door handles and light switches get covered with so many overlapping fingermarks that it is sometimes impossible to isolate those belonging to a particular individual.

Photographing prints in the early 1960's.

Fingerprints that have 'developed' on a bottle through the superglue technique.

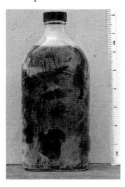

We have already seen how lasers and other light sources are used to 'paint' an area at the scene of a crime with special light which reveals the presence of prints without damaging them or the surface beneath. This equipment is also used in the laboratory, but forensic scientists have other techniques at their disposal. There are chemical processes which can reveal fingerprints on paper, for example. Sweat and grease from the finger sink into the porous surface of the paper, and when treated in a chemical bath, prints will become visible as stains on the paper.

One useful but unlikely method of revealing prints was discovered quite by accident. A broken photographic tank was being repaired using super-glue, and the next day, the glass tank was found to be covered with white fingerprints which had 'developed' overnight. The vapour from the glue reacts with the natural chemicals contained in sweat, and brings up a clear white print. This method can be used on many objects, especially where it would be difficult to dust for prints normally without destroying other prints. Sometimes a whole car is sealed in a tent and exposed to the vapours, effectively testing the whole car at once without touching it – although it must be admitted that the process does not do the car much good.

Fingerprinting a Corpse

Fingerprint identification is not only used to solve crimes, and one of its main uses is in identifying unknown bodies from accidents and major disasters. Prints are taken from the body of a victim, and then the forensic scientist will go to the home of someone feared killed in the accident to see if matching prints can be found among their personal effects. One bizarre aspect of such work can occur when an unknown corpse is recovered from water. If a body remains in water for a long time, the skin at first becomes wrinkly as it does when we stay in the bath or swimming pool too long. After a while, however, the layers of skin start to separate, and the surface epidermal layer comes away from the dermal layer beneath. On the hands of a corpse, this means the outer layers of skin separate like a glove, making it difficult to take fingerprints directly from the body. In

The Metropolitan Police now have computer records of 4,000,000 fingerprints.

Painstaking identification of fingerprints thirty years ago.

such cases, the forensic scientist will cut the skin around the wrist and remove the 'glove' of skin; then the 'glove' is simply slipped over the scientist's own gloved hand, and the prints are taken as if the skin belonged to the living fingers.

Examining and Matching Prints

Once a set of fingerprints has been obtained in any one of these ways, the process of examination begins. The prints are looked at with the naked eye and magnifying glass, and the relative positions of all the ridge forks and endings are noted. With the help of a computer, this information is turned into a numerical value, and stored digitally on a computer database. A video picture is also stored so that visual comparisons can easily be made later. When a new set of prints from a crime scene or body arrives, the information from each print is transformed into a set of numbers, and the computer searches its records for similar patterns. The database at New Scotland Yard In London contains the prints of about four

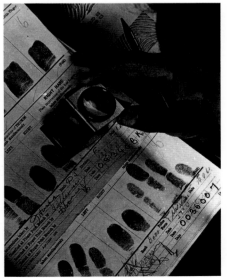

million people, and searching through all these by hand would obviously take far to long to be of any use in solving crimes – the criminal might die of old age before a match was located. The speed of the computerised system is invaluable. But the actual identification of matching prints does not rest with the computer; all it does is suggest an area within the database containing a number of similar patterns, which are then individually checked by experience fingerprints officers. The final identification is always made by the trained eye, not a machine.

The Christmas Eve Murder

What the fingerprints experts look for are the same characteristics in the same order on two separate prints. In the UK for legal purposes, a positive identification requires at least sixteen of these characteristics in common. It is possible to be fairly certain of a match with far fewer points of comparison, but for fingerprints to be used as evidence in court, a really conclusive identification is needed.

An example of the value of fingerprint evidence, and of the speed of the computer search, comes from a case of armed robbery a few years ago. It was the day before Christmas Eve when two men held up an Off Licence; during the raid, they shot and seriously injured a policeman. A team of forensics examiners spent most of the night at the scene gathering evidence, and returned to the laboratory on the morning of Christmas Eve. They brought back a great deal of possible evidence, but did not know which items might prove significant, and were resigned to a long and painstaking search through the items. At 10am that morning, a gun was found near the scene and brought to Scotland Yard In London for fingerprints testing; this revealed a good set of prints. However, a few hours later, the elimination prints of the person who had found the weapon arrived at the laboratory, and unfortunately these matched the prints found on the gun. The investigators were again faced with searching through an enormous quality of miscellaneous evidence, when luck showed them a more profitable path. A witness came forward to say that one of the gunmen had brought a white plastic bag to the scene – and such a bag had been recovered amongst all the other evidence.

By now it was late in the afternoon of Christmas Eve. The forensics team decided to use a new method of testing for prints on the bag, but this needed special equipment which took time to

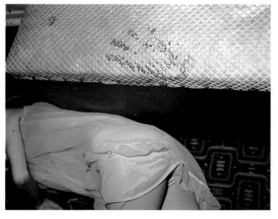

A bloody handprint on a table at the scene of a murder.

Putting a human 'glove' from a corpse onto the hand of a forensic scientist in order to obtain prints.

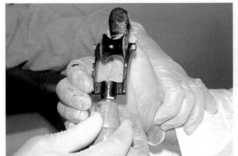

get ready. At 7pm the bag was placed in a vacuum chamber, and particles of metal were deposited on it to reveal any fingerprints. The results were good, producing an unusual combination of prints ideal for comparison by computer. But by now the computer had been powered down for the Christmas break, and staff had to be recalled from their homes to get it going. Eventually the prints were digitally coded and fed into the computer, which searched its whole database of some 40 million digits – and produced seven possible matches.

Fingerprints officers set about checking the suggested matches visually, and the third set they looked at was identical with the prints on the plastic bag. At one minute into Christmas Day, a name was put to the gunman, and this information was telephoned through to the local police. The named man was quickly arrested, and under interrogation he gave the name of his accomplice. Both received long prison sentences for the shooting and robbery, thanks to the expertise and facilities at the command of the forensic fingerprints department.

CHAPTER SEVEN

Piecing Together
the Physical Evidence

For a long time he remained there, turning over the leaves and dried sticks, gathering what seemed to me to be dust into an envelope and examining with his lens not only the ground, but even the bark of the tree as far as he could reach.
(THE BOSCOMBE VALLEY MYSTERY)

The analysis of physical evidence covers a wide range of possible items recovered from the scene, and among the most common types are soil, glass, paint, hair and fibres. Although we might think that human hairs and fibres from cloth are delicate and susceptible to decay, they can be remarkably long-lived; hairs and threads of linen from Egyptian mummies can still show all the distinguishing features that forensic scientists look for today. Much physical evidence will be very small, ranging from individual hairs to tiny fragments of paint, and a variety of highly sensitive tests and equipment can be brought to bear on even the most microscopic of samples.

Clues in the Soil

Although frequently found, soil and dirt samples may not be very informative. Soil types remain constant over quite large areas, and Sherlock Holmes' method of deduction would be regarded as very hit-and-miss today:
'You have come up from the south-west, I see.'

Soil samples are often collected from the shoes and clothes of both suspect and victim, as well as from the undercarriage of cars, especially if suspected of causing an accident; the impact of a crash or sudden braking may dislodge dirt stuck to the underside of a vehicle, and this can be tested against samples taken from the suspect car. Footmarks in soil are very useful because all shoes bear individual signs of damage caused by the way we walk. As with a bullet marked by the gun that fired it, a footmark can be traced to a particular shoe by the random pattern of damage on the sole. If soil from the scene is then found adhered to the shoe, the match is made even easier to prove.

Foreign bodies in soil are often as useful for identification purposes as the soil itself. In one case, a man broke into a house, walking through the chicken run on the way. Unfortunately for him, the owners had scattered small broken pieces of willow pattern plate in the chicken run for the birds to use as grit, and some of these fragments embedded themselves in the mud on his shoes. When the man was examined by the police, the little slivers of blue and white china at once connected him with the scene. So in this case, the soil was only important because of the unusual evidence it contained. In the same way, seeds and plant fibres in samples of earth can help link the soil more specifically with a particular location.

Evidence from plants can be important in its own right, of course; in 1989, minute traces of ivy helped to prove Trevor Tuck guilty of murder. The investigation started when the body of a child was found hidden under a quantity of ivy leaves. Suspicion fell on Tuck, and a set of newly-washed clothes was found at his house – but if he had hoped to destroy any incriminating evidence on the clothes, he was out of luck. Forensic Scientists tested the washed garments, and found fibres from the victim's clothes, along with traces of plant debris. Under the microscope, these traces were found to be identical with the minute, star-shaped hairs found growing on the underside of ivy leaves at the scene.

Policemen searching for bullets and murder clues outside Wormwood Scrubs prison.

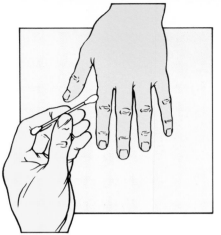

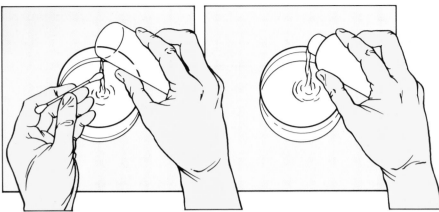

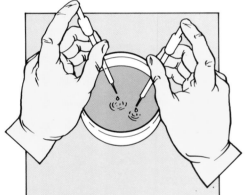

The Griess Test for Nitroglycerine:

*1. A swab is taken from the suspect's hands
2. The sample is washed into a dish
3. Caustic soda is added which 'liberates' any nitrates present in solution.
4. Sulphanilic acid and aromatic compounds are added. They form a purple dye if nitrites are present.*

Evidence from Glass

Another common and surprisingly informative type of evidence is glass from windows and light bulbs. An electron microscope can analyse fragments of glass from half a square millimetre right down to particles a tenth of a millimetre in size, so even the smallest piece of evidence can be persuaded to tell its tale. All glass is not the same; different types are used to make bottles, windows and drinking glasses, so if a suspect claims that slivers of glass on his clothes come from an accident with a milk bottle rather than a broken window at the scene of a burglary, this claim can easily be verified.

Glass is often examined when scientists are trying to trace vehicles involved in hit and run incidents, especially when the victim is killed and there are no witnesses. Fragments of smashed headlight are pieced together to reveal numbers embossed on the glass – these numbers identify the make and age of the car. And damage to a headlight bulb on a suspect car can show whether the light was on when the bulb was broken, indicating a night-time crash. If the metal filament was glowing when the bulb smashed, it will show distinctive oxidisation colouring caused by air penetrating the bulb and reacting with the hot metal of the filament. Another pointer that the light was on at the time of impact is that minuscule traces of melted glass will be fused onto the filament.

In cases where a gun has been fired through a window, the direction of the shot can be established by looking at the way the glass broke. The pieces of glass are fitted back together into a flat sheet, then the lines of fracture are examined in cross-section. The side of the window that the bullet hit first will show a slightly smaller area of damage than the side from which the bullet emerged – in cross-section, this looks like a cone spreading out from the point of impact through the thickness of the glass.

The Electron Microscope

The forensic science laboratory often deals with samples of paint; analysis of the colour and chemical composition can identify a painted weapon like an axe, or tell the police what sort of car they should be looking for. This sort of examination is carried out by a scanning electron microscope – a modern instrument of amazing sensitivity, and an important weapon in the armoury of the forensic scientist. The electron microscope has two uses: it produces a magnified image of the sample for visual comparison, and it can make a chemical analysis. This method has the great advantage of being non-destructive – at the end of the process, the sample has not been altered in any way, and can still be submitted to other tests, or produced as an exhibit in court.

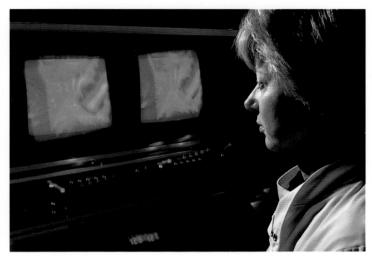

Examining minute fragments of glass from a suspect's garments under a scanning electron microscope.

The delicate flake of paint is mounted in a block of epoxy resin glue like araldite, which is sliced to give a cross-section through the paint. Then the whole block is placed in a vacuum chamber inside the microscope and bombarded with a beam of high-energy electrons. The image on an electron microscope is not produced by optical means, as with an ordinary light microscope; instead, a picture is produced by the action of the electrons. The electron beam scans across the sample, interacting with the surface of the paint and making it give back electrons, which strike two detectors within the chamber. These detectors interpret the results and produce a pair of highly-detailed images on two screens. The beam of electrons interacts differently with separate areas of the sample, so the final image shows a contrast between the individual layers of paint.

But the scanning electron microscope is not just useful for visualising minute pieces of evidence at high magnification; it can also chemically analyse the sample, giving a separate read-out for each layer of paint in turn. When the electron beam scans across the surface of the paint flake, the electrons bounce back to make up the image on the screen – but x-rays are also produced in the process, and these can give a breakdown of the paint's composition. The energy of the x-rays depends on the chemical elements that make up the sample, and a detector measures this energy to produce a chart of the elements present. In this way, if many layers of paint in a flake recovered from the scene show the same colour and chemical composition as the layers on a suspect's car, a match can be made.

51

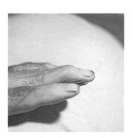

A single, damning hair of the murderer left in the fingernail of his victim.

Analysing Hairs

An electron microscope can also be used to examine individual hairs; a single hair can be split lengthwise and magnified until the image is about ten centimetres wide, revealing enormous variations between hairs coming from different species. Although it is unlikely that a human hair would be mistaken for one from an animal, it is often important to differentiate between animal species. For instance, in cases of suspected badger-baiting, a suspect may claim that hairs found on his clothes came legitimately from a dog, so the forensic scientist has to prove the hairs belonged to a badger before they can be used as evidence. Human hairs are a more common type of evidence, though, and they can reveal a great deal about the person they came from, and the manner in which they were shed.

A single hair can tell a scientist the race and sex of a person; sex can be established using the same method applied to dental pulp, where a sample of cells is stained so that only components from male cells fluoresce under a special light. Again, the scanning electron microscope can show whether the hair was cut or pulled out – indeed, it can even tell the difference between hairs cut by scissors, a scalpel or a blunt knife. When scissors are used, the hair shows a distinct pinching effect where the blades have gripped before the cut is made; with a scalpel, the hair is cut cleanly; but with a blunter knife the cut will be slightly ragged. If the hair has been torn out, the root may still be attached, or the ripped end will be very ragged indeed. This sort of information is most important in cases of violent attack or sexual assault. If a victim complains of having hair torn out by an attacker, ragged breaks in the hair will strongly point to an act of violence, but smoothly cut hair will suggest that the tale of assault has been embellished or invented, and that the complainant has cut his or her own hair to colour the story.

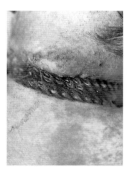

The mark left on a victim's neck after he had been hung by a dog-lead.

Occasionally, hairs can provide evidence in cases of poisoning by arsenic. It is possible for a person to take quite large amounts of arsenic without dying – the symptoms can be mistaken for a ruptured gastric ulcer or inflammation of the appendix – and so a would-be poisoner may have to make several attempts at murder by arsenic. In non-fatal doses, traces of arsenic are excreted into the fingernails and hair. As the hair and nails grow, they carry these traces along in their tissues as a permanent record. From the position of such traces along the length of a hair, it is possible to tell the approximate dates when the poison was given.

Fibres

Fibres from clothing or furnishings are perhaps the commonest type of physical evidence presented to the forensic laboratory, because they are so easy to shed and pick up accidentally. The mutual transfer of tiny threads between an attacker and victim, or a burglar and the house he robs, needs no great violence; and the alien fibre may never be noticed until it is removed by the forensic scientist. Many such threads are only two or three millimetres long, but they can sometimes indicate the occupation of the person they came from, and can usually be persuaded to reveal the type of fibre and the chemical composition of any dye present. When a suspect garment arrives at the laboratory, the surface is covered with strips of transparent adhesive tape which are peeled off to remove any loose fibres; the strips of tape are attached to clear plastic strips for microscopic examination. (One garment can produce a square metre of tape bearing specimens, each of which must be looked at through the microscope; this gives some idea of the scale of the forensic scientist's task.) Most of these fibres will be of no importance, but those which look significant are mounted individually on microscope slides. Now a series of tests begins, revealing ever more detailed information in the search for a positive match.

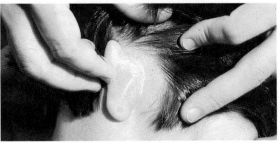

Blood-red mottling behind the ears characteristic of pressure on the neck on the body of a rape victim.

The Infra-Red Spectrophotometer

First a comparison microscope is used to look at the suspect fibre side by side with one from the scene, and a simple visual comparison is made of colour, width, and so on. If the match appears good, the process is repeated using different types of light; some colours look the same under ordinary white light, but react differently to ultra-violet and blue light, showing they come from different sources. At this stage it is easy enough to identify natural fibres like cotton and wool just from their appearance under the microscope, but artificial fibres all have a similar appearance, and a special test is needed to tell nylon from acrylic or polyester. A complex piece of equipment called an infra-red spectrophotometer is linked to a microscope to look at the individual fibre. As its name suggests, this technique uses infra-red wavelengths of light, in effect invisible heat energy, to tell which chemicals go to make up a man-made fibre. A chart is produced, showing peaks and troughs which identify the characteristic chemical bonds in different polymers, like polyester, allowing the scientists to put a name to the fabric their test fibre came from.

Having identified the type of fibre, attention turns to the dye that colours it. Pure colours are actually made up of a mixture of separate hues, and in a variation of the previous test, these colour components can be told apart. With a micro-spectrophotometer, the sample fibre is illuminated by the visible spectrum of light, and some of the wavelengths of light are absorbed more than others by the dye. The different patterns of absorption give a very precise definition of the dye

Tyre marks on an accident victim's leg.

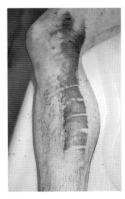

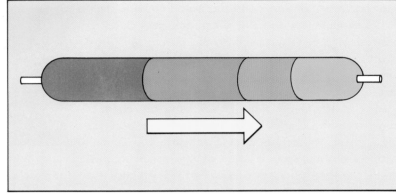

The GCMS (Gas Chromatography/ Mass Spectrometry) test:

1. A swab is taken.
2. The chemical constituents of the swab are passed down a tube packed with liquid-coated material. Only components of a known mass arrive at the detector end: often traces are too small to be conclusive and could also result from chemicals on a smoker's hand.

colours present. The device is so sensitive that it can spot minute variations between batches of the same dye, caused by slight inconsistencies during manufacture. Apart from its sensitivity, this method is also non-destructive, so the suspect fibre is still intact at the end.

Thin Layer Chromatography

A final test adds yet another check to the process of accurate fibre matching, although it also alters the fibre. Thin layer chromatography involves physically separating the individual dye colours from the fibre. The dye is extracted from a single suspect fibre into a solution, and this is deposited as a series of spots on a glass plate coated with silica gel. When dry, a solvent liquid is applied to the plate below the spots of dye. This liquid runs up the plate by capillary action, dissolving the dye components and carrying them along: each component travels a different, characteristic, distance. The result is a series of colour bands, and the location of each band indicates its chemical composition.

It may seem that so many tests, often producing the same results by different means, are a waste of time and money, but the forensic scientist would disagree. Each test which matches a suspect fibre with one from the scene increases the value of the evidence, and makes the possibility of error more remote. Even when all these sophisticated tests produce a positive match, the forensic scientist remains a cautious animal:

A forensic toxicologist establishing the contents of a suspected drug sample through mass-spectrometry.

the laboratory is likely to report that the suspect fibre comes from this garment – or another exactly like it.

Trapping 'The Fox'

Several sorts of physical evidence were used in the early 1980s to track down a cunning and violent rapist known as the Fox. The man caused widespread fear for some time, threatening his victims with a shotgun and raping them in their own homes. The Fox was a careful criminal, wearing a mask to prevent his victims describing him, but on several occasions the mark of a shoe was found at the scene by the police. Forensic scientists examined the footmarks and identified a particular type of shoe; they even went out and bought an identical pair, so the police would know what style of uppers to look for when interviewing suspects. This evidence might have been enough to trap the Fox, had he not been an especially careful and devious man – after every few attacks, he burned the clothes and shoes, he had used, and wore a new set to commit his next offence.

Examining a suspect training shoe for comparison with prints left at the scene.

A magnified fragment of house paint taken from the clothes of a burglar. It shows the layers of repainting and can be conclusively matched with paint from the burgled house.

But every contact leaves a trace, and during one attack he left behind a different type of physical evidence for the forensics department to work on. On his way to commit one rape, he left his car in a copse just off the road, and this place was linked with the crime. From the size of the clearing and the position of tyre tracks, the size and shape of his car were estimated. A painstaking search, rather in the manner of Sherlock Holmes with his lens, also revealed a smear of paint on the bark of a tree where the car had nudged against it. The paint flakes were analysed, the type of paint was traced, and this knowledge was added to the information about the car's size, until an astoundingly detailed description could be given – the police should look for a harvest gold coloured Allegro car.

Two police officers later went to conduct a routine interview with a man to see if he could be eliminated from their inquiries, and they arrived to find him working on his car. It was a gold Allegro, and showed signs of damage exactly where the laboratory had predicted they would be found. The presence of this car was enough to have the man questioned at the police station, and the next day he confessed to the series of rapes.

So the evidence provided by the tiniest traces of material can be used to build up a remarkably accurate picture of a wanted man or his possessions, despite the criminal's most careful precautions.

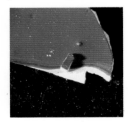

Pathology: The Science of Unexpected Death

Medical pathology involves looking for the natural causes of injury and illness, while forensic pathology is the investigation of unexpected, suspicious and criminal causes of death or injury. This process of investigation begins at the scene, and continues with the post mortem examination, or autopsy.

Pathology at the Scene

At the scene, the relationship of the body to its surroundings can tell the forensic pathologist a good deal – and what looks highly suspicious to a police officer may have an obvious natural explanation for an experienced pathologist. For example, in one case an old man was found dead in his flat; he was naked and his body was covered with small injuries, suggesting some kind of assault. In addition, all the cupboards and drawers in the flat were open and the contents were strewn about, as if the rooms had been ransacked by an intruder. In fact, however, the old man had died of hypothermia, and all the circumstances surrounding his death were easily explained by a Home Office pathologist. Hypothermia often makes its victims confused, so they may wander about, opening cupboards at random and banging into furniture, causing various injuries. Also, in the middle stages of hypothermia, the sufferers often feel very warm, and may remove all their clothing, which explains the old man's nakedness – this condition is called 'paradoxical undressing'.

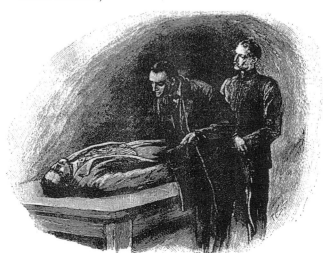

The analytical techniques available to the forensic scientist have become more and more sophisticated, but the actual examination of the body has changed little over the years; pathologists still rely on their hands, their eyes, and the amassed experience of their profession.

The Post Mortem

The post mortem takes place in the mortuary, and its purpose is to provide answers to a series of questions. How long has the person been dead? Has the body been moved after death? What was the cause of death, and were all the injuries caused while the person was still alive? The pathologist also looks for any clues which might help identify a possible killer, like bite marks or shoe prints on the body.

Establishing the time of death is not the simple business often portrayed in detective fiction, and although educated estimations can be made, in up to 10% of cases the suggested time of death is inaccurate to the point of being misleading. Ideally, the temperature of the body is taken repeatedly over several hours to assess the rate of cooling, but this is only valid for the first 12 to 18 hours after death; in the first 12 hours, though, the time of death can be stated to within two or three hours. Many factors can influence a body's rate of cooling, from the presence of draughts or thick clothing to the relative fatness or thinness of the body. Contrary to popular belief, rigor mortis does not suggest an exact time of death; this stiffening of all the muscles in the body is variable in its onset and duration, and so must be cited as evidence with caution. Rigor mortis usually lasts for 36 to 48 hours, but it can pass off in only a few hours, and has been known to last for five days – though both these extremes are rare.

Examining the Skin

The forensic pathologist spends more time examining the surface of a body than its interior, because this is where most information is usually found. Every stage is recorded with photographs, diagrams and notes, and such records will be kept throughout a pathologist's career. The skin of a corpse may be examined with a handlens, and ultra-violet light is used to show up marks more clearly. From the pattern of injury, it is possible to reconstruct what happened before death, even to the extent of recreating the course of an attack and saying how many assailants were involved. Bruising may show if the victim was held by one person while another caused more major injuries; such

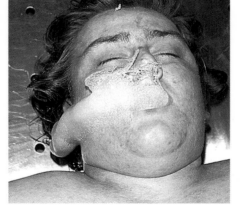

Foaming from the mouth and nose characteristic of death by drowning.

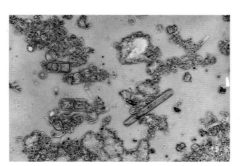

(left) The presence of a significant number of diatoms (silica-shelled photosynthesizing organisms) in the human lung and kidney tissue of a body recovered from water indicates that the body was alive when it entered the water. Diatoms are absorbed by breathing, not by passive diffusion. Few diatoms in body tissue suggest that the body was already dead when it entered the water.

A murder made to look like suicide: the man was shot, and the shotgun left on the bed, but the arms of the body are under the blankets.

restraint marks often take some time to develop in a dead body, just as in a living one, so the body must be looked at again a few days after the initial examination. Indeed, some bruises never appear on the skin's surface, but they can be detected in the tissues beneath by dissection, which reveals characteristic marks.

Disguising Murder as Suicide

Faced with the reality of a corpse, a killer will quite often try to make a murder look like an accident or suicide, but it is hard to deceive the forensic pathologist. One such case occurred in West Africa, where an Englishman working there was found dead on the rough ground outside his block of flats. It was at first thought that he had committed suicide, because there were apparently self-inflicted cuts on his arms, and blood was found in his bath; the supposition was that he had tried to slit his wrists in the bath, then jumped to his death from the balcony of his flat. But the findings of the post mortem revealed a very different scenario. To begin with, the wounds on the arms could only have been caused by someone else, because the cuts were made in the wrong direction to be self-inflicted. And the body only showed limited bruising from the supposed impact of the fall, suggesting that the man was dead long before he hit the ground. On the other hand, there was very severe bruising on the back of the head, which was obviously caused before death. The forensic pathologist eventually reconstructed the crime as follows: the man was struck on the head while lying in bed, probably with a large frying pan found on the bed. Then the body was moved to the bath, where the killer cut the arms to simulate suicide. Finally, the body was dumped onto the waste ground, to make it look as if the man had jumped.

Inside the Corpse

After the whole body surface has been examined, the pathologist's attention moves on to the internal organs; every organ is carefully studied and dissected for signs of injury, disease, or traces of poison. Some poisons are very difficult to spot at post mortem, and these may only be discovered if a suspicion of poisoning already exists, when the tissues will be chemically analysed. Obvious signs of suicidal or homicidal poisoning are the remains of tablets in the mouth or stomach, and the presence of injection marks which cannot be explained by any attempts to resus-

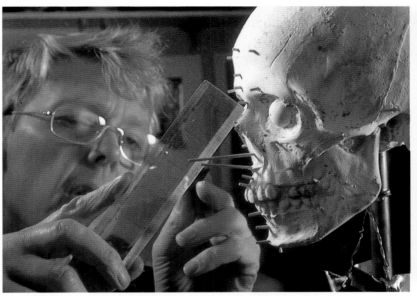

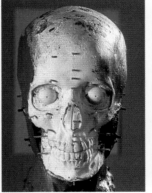

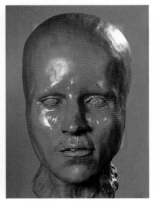

citate the victim in hospital. Many poisons act on the area of the brain which controls respiration, and so the forensic pathologist will be on the lookout for changes in the body which suggest the sudden and unexplained onset of heart and respiratory failure.

The internal organs may also show damage caused by stabbing or bullet entry, and this will enable the examiner to assess the length of blade used, or the direction from which a shot was fired. Killers quite often try to disguise their deed by burning the corpse, but it is rare for a body to be totally consumed by fire; even if the outer surface is charred beyond recognition, the internal organs often survive, still showing tears and blood-clotting, the characteristic signs of injury.

The extraordinary stages of reconstruction of an unknown victim's head from measurements and projections from her skull.

59

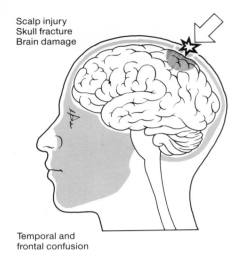

Scalp injury
Skull fracture
Brain damage

Temporal and
frontal confusion

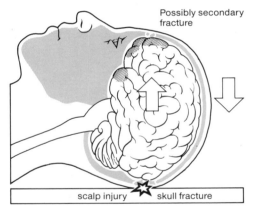

Possibly secondary
fracture

scalp injury   skull fracture

'Coup' injuries to the
stationary head and
opposite the point of
impact on a falling
head .

Head Injuries

It is possible to tell the cause of head injuries by examining the brain after death, to see the location of damage in relation to the external point of impact. If someone is struck directly on the head, say with a hammer, the brain is damaged immediately below the place where the blow fell; this is called a 'coup' (strike) injury. But if the victim falls and his head hits the ground, the brain injury will be on the opposite side to the external damage. This is a 'contre-coup' (counter-strike) injury – the damage to the delicate brain tissue is in fact caused by the rapid deceleration of the head when it hits the ground, not by the impact itself.

The knowledge of this phenomenon helped clear a young man suspected of a murderous attack in London. He admitted he had been in an argument, and claimed that during a scuffle he pushed the victim, who fell and struck his head. The victim had a wound on the back of his head, and the police suspected that the young man might have beaten him with a blunt weapon. At the post mortem, however, the classic signs of contre-coup injury were discovered at the front of the victim's brain, opposite the external wound, and the suspect's story was confirmed.

Analysing a Skeleton

Sometimes the forensic pathologist is confronted with nothing more than a skeleton, which can be less than informative. It is easy enough to estimate height and build from the size of the bones and the markings where muscles were attached, but telling the age of a skeleton can be more difficult. Once the body has stopped growing in early adulthood, few changes occur in the bones, and it can be impossible to differentiate between the skeleton of a twenty-five year old and a person of fifty.

The climate and burial customs in England mean than skeletons can survive intact for many hundreds of years, but in parts of Africa it has been known for bones to decay only two or three years after burial. And while it is usual for the soft body tissues to disappear fairly quickly, under some conditions the whole body may be preserved. This occurs occasionally when a body is immersed in a bog for many years, or buried in desert sand. One macabre case came to light in 1960, when the celebrated forensic pathologist Professor Francis Camps helped solve the mystery surrounding a case of natural mummification.

The 'Mummy of Rhyl'

In the seaside town of Rhyl on the north Wales coast, Mrs. Sarah Jane Harvey had taken in lodgers for many years. In May 1960, the elderly Mrs. Harvey had to go into hospital for cancer tests, and her son decided to decorate the house in her absence. In the process he opened a locked cupboard on the landing – and in it he saw what looked like a mummified foot. The police were called, confirmed the presence of a mummified body, and did their best to remove the mummy, which was firmly stuck to the floor of the cupboard. In the end, the well-preserved body was freed with the aid of a garden spade, and removed for a belated post mortem. X-rays of the skeleton suggested it was the corpse of a middle-aged woman, and a preliminary examination of the curled-up body revealed a groove around the neck, with a knotted length of stocking still adhering to the skin.

The stiffened 'mummy' was soaked in a glycerine solution to soften the tissues, straightened out, and carefully examined: most of the internal organs had decayed, but there were no signs of injury or bruising, beyond the mark on the neck. Strangely, the hair on the head was no more than stubble a few millimetres long, with clean-cut ends. All the appearances pointed to the unknown woman having been murdered by strangulation, her hair having been cut after death, and the body hidden in the cupboard, where it slowly dried out. Mrs. Harvey was charged with murder.

When questioned, Mrs. Harvey admitted that a semi-invalid woman, Mrs. Frances Knight, had come to lodge with her during World War II, and that this was her body. But she denied having killed her lodger, and explained that one night Mrs. Knight started screaming with pain and rolling on the floor in her nightdress. Mrs. Harvey went downstairs to make the woman a cup of tea, but when she returned, she had found her lodger dead. Frightened and alone, Mrs. Harvey said she hid the body in the cupboard and locked it, telling no-one what had happened. She continued to collect a weekly payment of £2 for Mrs. Knight, as she had done when the woman was alive. When the Magistrate's clerk who made the payment inquired from time to time about Mrs. Knight's condition, Mrs. Harvey managed to give the impression that her lodger's health had its ups and downs, but that she was definitely alive.

This story would have seemed more believable, had it not been for the groove around the corpse's neck, caused by the tightness of the tied stocking (the criss-cross pattern of the stocking material was even visible printed on the skin), and the

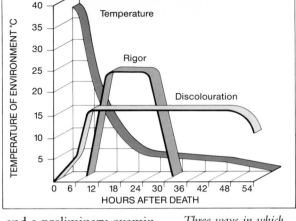

Three ways in which lapse of time after death can be measured: by the fall in body temperature, the onset of lapsing of rigor mortis (very variable) and the extent of discoloration. More accurate methods now include tests on body fluids, the contents of the stomach and surface of the teeth.

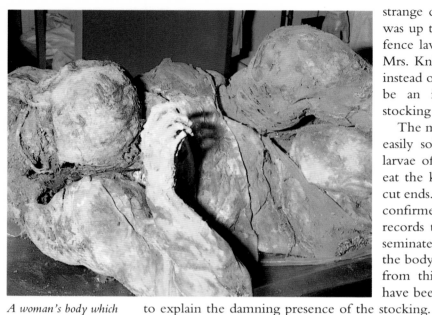

A woman's body which had been hidden under sacking and mummified under the right conditions of dry warmth and protection from the air.

strange circumstance of the cut hair. It was up to Professor Camps and the defence lawyers to show two things: that Mrs. Knight could have died of disease instead of violence, and that there could be an innocent explanation for the stocking around her neck.

The mystery of the cut hair was quite easily solved – it was shown that the larvae of the brown clothes moth may eat the keratin in hair, leaving cleanly-cut ends. As for the cause of death, it was confirmed from Mrs. Knight's medical records that she had been ill with disseminated sclerosis, and the position of the body was typically found in sufferers from this disease. So the death could have been natural, and it only remained to explain the damning presence of the stocking.

Then an old folk custom was recalled, in which a sick person would tie and old, unwashed sock or stocking round their neck. This custom was once widespread across the country, but was it still practised? Apparently so, for when the suggestion was put forward in court, many whispers and glances were exchanged amongst the spectators, who were obviously admitting the practice to their neighbours. It was still needed to account for the tightness of the stocking around the deceased's neck, and Francis Camps suggested the following course of events. The body was hidden with the stocking still tied loosely round the neck, and for a few days the normal processes of putrefaction continued before the body began to dry out. So the stocking was first stuck to the skin by the products of decomposition; then gas formed in the body, making it swell and stretching the stocking tightly round the neck to form a groove. Finally the gas dispersed, the swelling subsided, but the stocking remained stuck to the skin, imprinting its pattern on the wet tissues, which took some time to dry out. This bizarre but plausible scenario was accepted by the jury, who cleared Mrs. Harvey of murder, but found her guilty of falsely obtaining £2 a week on behalf of the dead woman.

This unusual case is just one example of how the forensic pathologist's detailed knowledge of the way body tissues behave under all sorts of different circumstances can unravel the most baffling occurrence. There is no doubt that Mrs. Harvey was a proficient liar, and that she covered up the death of her lodger effectively for many years, but expert evidence showed that she was not a murderess.

CHAPTER NINE

Biology: The Unique Evidence of DNA

Biological specimens can tell a great deal about the people they come from, and they often provide an important link in the chain of information which leads to identification. The presence of various chemicals in the blood can tie a suspect very strongly to a crime – but so far it is impossible to make a positive identification on the basis of blood group information alone. Scientists can conclusively exclude someone from their blood group, but when it comes to positive identification, they can only say "it is extremely unlikely that sample X came from anyone but suspect X".

In the past few years, developments in the field of genetics have been adopted by forensic scientists, and the concept of 'DNA profiling' has attracted keen attention. This technique uses the genetic material from our cells to produce an unique pattern; only identical twins share the same DNA profile. Although this method of identification is not routinely used, it has already produces some spectacular results.

Holmes held up a crumpled branch of flowering gorse. To my horror I perceived that the yellow blossoms were all dabbled with crimson. On the path, too, and among the heather were dark stains of clotted blood.

(THE PRIORY SCHOOL)

Identifying Stains

When faced with a bloodstain the forensic biologist has to answer a series of increasingly specific questions. Is the stain blood? Is it human in origin? What blood groups and other chemical information can be identified in the sample? The presence of blood is detected with the Kastle-Meyer test, which involves pressing a piece of filter paper onto the suspect stain, then testing this paper, leaving the original stain intact. The Kastle-Meyer test uses a chemical, phenolphthalein, which turns bright pink when blood is present. This sort of technique is called a presumptive test, because a positive result is presumed to be blood; but this must be checked by more specific tests.

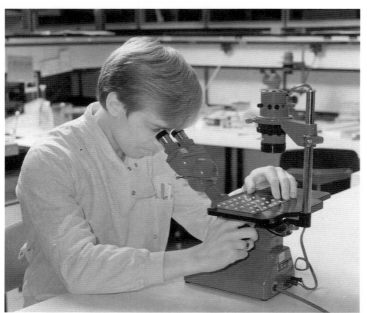

A pathologist reading the results from a testing of blood groups from blood stains.

Blood Groups

The ABO system of blood grouping is the mainstay of forensic blood testing. The system is based on the detection of various proteins, called antigens, in the walls of red blood cells. These antigens are named A and B, and a person's blood group can be described as either A or B, AB or O (containing neither antigen). In the blood, the A and B antigens are accompanied by antibodies of the opposite group, which are found in the plasma surrounding the cells – this opposition is important, because when antigens and antibodies of the same group mix, their reaction makes the red blood cells combine into clumps, with fatal results. So a group A person will have b antibodies in the plasma, and vice versa; a group AB person will have neither a nor b, and a group O person will have both a and b antibodies. The ABO grouping of a bloodstain is determined by adding the a and b antibodies, and seeing which reacts with the blood cells: if a antibodies cause a reaction, then the blood is of group A. Of course, as group O contains neither A nor B antigens, it can only be distinguished in this test by a negative result, which could equally be caused by technical failure. Luckily, another test for group O exists, which coincidentally uses and extract of gorse seeds – the plant on which Sherlock Holmes found bloodstains in The Priory School.

In up to 80% of people, the blood group antigens are also present in other body fluids like saliva, semen, sweat and urine. These secretions can be detected, and so a person's blood group can be discovered without them having shed any blood at all. Those people called 'non-secretors' do have some antigens in their body fluids, but too little to register on the tests; but the blood group of a 'secretor' may be told even from traces of saliva round a bite mark.

The PGM Blood-typing System

There are many other systems for blood-typing, based on other proteins and enzymes in the blood. One of the most frequently used is the PGM (phosphoglucomutase) system, which detects combinations of up to ten types of an enzyme. Here the bloodstain is extracted from clothing or a weapon into water, and the solution is spotted onto a plate covered with gel. An electrical voltage is applied, making the individual enzymes migrate different distances along the plate; the result is invisible to the eye, but the application of a chemical developer reveals a track of lines, rather like a barcode, showing the enzymes' final positions. This technique, using an electric current to stimulate movement through the gel, is called electrophoresis; there is a variation which uses an acidity gradient across the plate to separate the enzymes, known as iso-electric focusing.

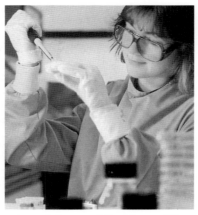

Taking DNA from a blood sample.

DNA Profiling

Much has been made recently of the accuracy and usefulness of DNA profiling from samples of body cells, and it is true that this is the only biological technique which permits positive identification of an individual. Even so, there is still a place for conventional blood group testing in the forensic science laboratory. For a start it is quicker and cheaper than DNA testing, and the variety of methods make it very broad-ranging as well as sensitive. Most important, however, are the sizes of samples needed for the two techniques: DNA tests require at least 20 microlitres, but preferably nearer 100 microlitres, while the PGM test needs only one or two microlitres. (A microlitre is a millionth of a litre.)

Nonetheless, despite its disadvantages and the short time it has been in use, DNA profiling has already proved one of the most valuable tools available to the forensic scientist. It produces a so-called DNA 'fingerprint', a visual representation of the unique genetic blueprint stored in each of our cells. Although it can be used on any biological sample containing enough cells, DNA profiling is most commonly used on samples of semen from cases of rape.

Inserting a sample of DNA into a gene scanner machine.

The first stage of the tests is to make sure that a suspect stain does in fact come from semen. The presumptive test for seminal fluid looks for an enzyme, acid phosphatase, which produces

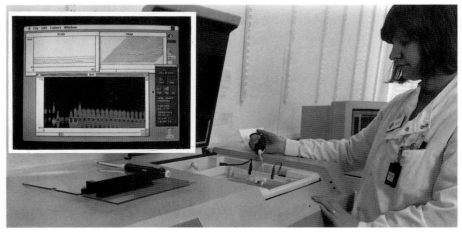

a purple colour if present. Semen consists of a liquid seminal plasma in which the spermatozoa themselves are suspended, and each of these parts is used for different tests; the seminal plasma is tested for the ABO and PGM blood group substances, and only the actual sperm heads are used for DNA profiling, because this is where the genetic material is found.

The seminal stain is extracted into water, and a soapy buffer solution may be used to remove the cellular debris from the sample; then this liquid is spun in a centrifuge to separate the solid material from the fluid. The long chain of DNA is cut up into different fragments by an enzyme which acts like chemical scissors, cutting the DNA at specific sequences along its length. Each sample contains an incredible amount of genetic information, although the scientists are only interested in a particular areas of this. The mixed up lengths of DNA are separated by putting the sample in a gel – when electrophoresis is applied, the current makes the lengths of DNA move through the gel towards the positive electrode. Their final position depend on their size, as the smallest pieces can move faster, and therefore further, than the longer lengths. Finally, special radioactively-labelled sequences of DNA are added; these stick to the sequences the scientists want to examine, so that they will show up on a x-ray film of the sample. The resulting picture shows two

DNA strands are extracted from samples and 'cut up' into pieces. These are put into gel and separated by electric current. After a radioactive probe is applied, which sticks to DNA sequences, a film reveals the DNA profile. (bottom) Shows two cases of doubtful identity.
1) The bands have shifted – are they from different samples?
2) The bands match.
3) Bands match but extra bands are present – again, due to different samples?

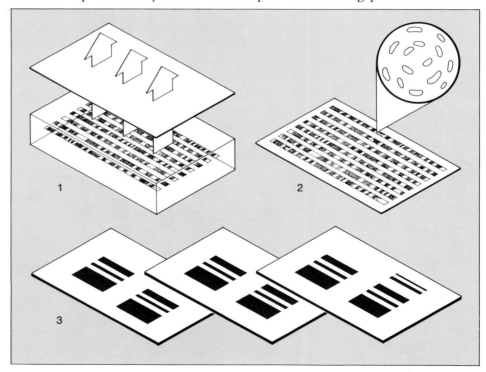

separate lines of bands for each person, one inherited from their mother and one from their father, and it is these bands which form the DNA profile.

For example, stains on a towel from the scene of a rape produced a set of four bands, indicating that biological material from two people was present; blood samples were taken from the victim and the man suspected of the attack, and these new DNA profiles confirmed that two bands from the towel came from each of them. Such conclusive evidence makes it impossible for a man to claim he was nowhere near the scene of an offence. Unfortunately, now that it is possible to prove that intercourse with a certain person did take place, many men accused of rape defend themselves by saying that the woman gave her consent – and consent is much more difficult to disprove.

The DNA bands produced from the original stain are compared with others made by samples taken from a suspect, and if the lines of bands match up, it can positively be said that they both came from the same person. Although the information stored in the whole length of a person's DNA is unique, for reasons of time and cost the forensic laboratory only tests certain small sections of this information, in order to make sure that the short lengths they examine could not be mistaken for DNA from someone else. Three separate tests are done, and the identification is only accepted when all three matches between sample and suspect are confirmed.

The National DNA Index

DNA profiles from criminal cases are stored on a national index, which so far contains about 1200 profiles. It is possible that one day the national index will carry the DNA profiles of every male in the country. (Although the police

Analysis of body fluids taken from a murder victim.

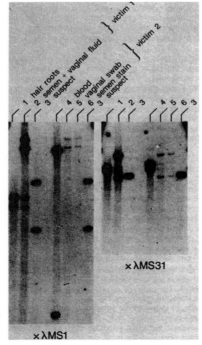

A completed DNA profile.

Professor Alec Jeffreys, the pioneer of DNA profiling, holds up a completed case for examination.

Bacteria containing synthetic human DNA are grown in cell cultures at the biology research centre at Alderley Park, UK, in order to examine target proteins.

and forensic scientists seem unofficially in favour of such a scheme which would make their task of identifying violent crimes such as rape and murder infinitely easier, other groups condemn such proposals as a violation of personal rights.)

As with fingerprints, the visual information is coded into numerical form and stored as a set of digits on the computer. When a new profile is fed in, the computer points out 'near matches', but the final identification always rests with the experts. The use of information from DNA is especially useful when the forensic scientists are trying to solve cases of sexual assault and rape, because the men who commit these offences often strike more than once; if two apparently separate cases can be linked by DNA profiles, then all the available evidence can be brought together in one investigation.

DNA Sampling at Work

The most well-known British case solved by DNA profiling involved a double murder in Leicestershire. In 1986 a young man was arrested for the sexual assault and murder of a teenage girl, and the police also suspected him of committing a very similar sexual murder in the same area three years before. There were semen samples available from both scenes, and DNA profiles made from from these samples showed that the two cases were linked – but they also showed that the suspect in custody was not responsible for the crimes. In January 1987 a major police operation began; it involved screening blood samples from the entire male population of a village and its surroundings, about 5000 men in all.

Conventional blood grouping tests eliminated a large proportion of these specimens, but even so 500 samples were sent for DNA testing. The murderer did live in the area, but he tried to deceive the authorities by paying another man to give a blood sample in his name, knowing that his own blood would betray him. This subterfuge was detected, however, and when the man was confronted, he at once confessed to both murders – and his DNA profile was shown to match the semen samples recovered from the bodies of the two victims.

In America, the case of People v. Wesley in 1989 was even more convoluted. Wesley was suspected of a particularly unpleasant crime, the murder by strangulation, rape and attempted sodomy of a mentally handicapped woman of 79. Unfortunately, the semen samples from the victim's body did not contain enough cellular material to make an effective comparison with Wesley's DNA profile. The forensic scientists turned instead to bloodstains on the man's clothing – if these stains could be shown to come from the victim, it would provide good evidence against Wesley. The scientists tried to obtain samples of blood from the victim, but unusually no such samples appeared to have been taken at the post mortem. Instead, they had to make a DNA profile from the roots of the woman's hair, which had been saved, and this showed that blood from the man's clothes had indeed been shed by the victim. In January 1989, Wesley was found guilty of murder, rape, attempted sodomy and burglary – without the DNA test, there is no way this horrible crime could have been traced to its source.

Inventive Reconstruction: The Dairy and Moorland Murders

Forensic biologists do not just perform highly sensitive tests to a set formula, though; sometimes they are faced with unusual problems which call for invention rather than well-known techniques. In one case a little girl was admitted to hospital with a ruptured stomach, and her body was found to be full of water. Her stepfather, a cowman, said he had been hosing down the dairy when the girl stepped in front of the hose, swallowing a lot of water. The forensic scientist was suspicious, however, and made his own investigations to test the stepfather's story. First he obtained various x-rays of children's stomachs to assess their size, then he found some pig's stomachs of the same size (pigs are physically very like humans, so their stomachs would be likely to behave as the girl's had done under similar circumstances). The forensic biologist wired these pig stomachs onto taps, which were running at the

Examining a difficult moorland site for clues to a murder.

same rate as the dairy hose, and found how much water they could take before bursting. From this he was able to calculate how long the little girl must have been swallowing water from her stepfather's hose. The result of these novel but carefully-conducted tests was the certainty that this was no accident – the man must have forced his stepdaughter to swallow water until her stomach ruptured under the strain.

On another occasion, the body of a woman was found on moorland, and the police needed to know whether she had been killed at the site, or murdered elsewhere and her body dumped later. The

Examining a sample of DNA in gel under ultra-violet light.

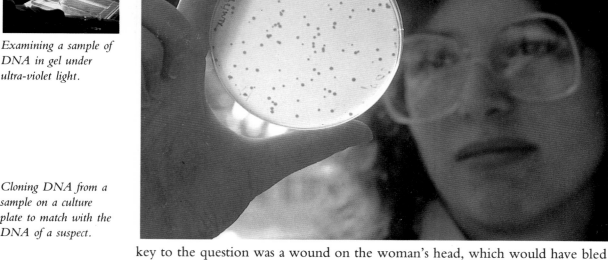

Cloning DNA from a sample on a culture plate to match with the DNA of a suspect.

key to the question was a wound on the woman's head, which would have bled profusely – if she had died where her body was found, there should be a large volume of blood at the scene, but if the body had been dumped there after death, there would be little blood. The problem was to assess how much blood was present in the soil beneath the woman's head. A forensic biologist took two squares of turf from the scene, one from under the head and the other from beside the body; the first was soaked with blood, and the second was clean. A chemical test revealed the extent of bloodstaining in the first piece of turf, and then animal blood was added to the clean turf until the area of staining was the same in the two samples. From this experiment it was possible to say that about half a pint of blood had soaked into the soil from the body, so the woman must have met her death on the moor – a dead body dumped there could not have shed so much blood.

These rather gruesome cases show that ingenuity and an open mind are as important to the forensic scientist as technical knowledge. The role of the forensic science laboratory is to reconstruct what happened at a scene from all the available evidence, no matter how strange or unpleasant. The scientist's job is not to confirm the police view of a case, but to discover and present the truth, using experience and expertise to ask questions of inanimate objects.

CHAPTER TEN

Entomology:
The Evidence of Insects

The entomologist's knowledge of insects has been used for forensic purposes since before the time of Sherlock Holmes, and it is still called upon today as a last resort in placing the time of a death. When a body has lain undiscovered for some time, the normal process of decay may make it impossible for a pathologist to estimate when the person died, or when the body was disposed of.

The Role of the Entomologist

This is when the forensic entomologist steps in to examine any insect eggs, maggots or beetles found on the corpse. An understanding of the habits and lifecycles of such creatures can date a recent corpse to within a day or two of death, while an older body can be tentatively dated to a particular month or year. Scientists have identified up to eight separate 'waves' of insect action on a corpse – as the body decays over the days and months, different types of insect attack in succession according to their tastes, beginning with flies like bluebottles, and graduating on to flesh-eating beetles.

The first recorded case involving forensic entomology was in the 1850s, when the body of a newborn baby was found hidden in a wall cavity near the chimney of a house. Two bricks had been removed to insert the tiny body, which was mummified when it was found. There was a population of moths living and breeding on the body, and a study of the larvae and adult moths showed that the death must have taken place some two years previously. This was important, because it cleared three recently arrived tenants of any involvement in the matter: in fact, the evidence pointed to a woman who had lived in the house before the new tenants, and who was known to have been pregnant. This woman was found and charged with infanticide, but it could only be

Cases of butterflies and moths flanked each side of the entrance. A large table was littered with all sorts of debris, while the tall brass tube of a powerful microscope bristled up amongst them.
(THE ADVENTURE OF THE THREE GARRIDEBS)

proved that she had hidden her baby's body, not that she had killed the child.

The Stages of Decay

Samples of insects should be taken from a corpse for careful examination, because many species are superficially similar but have different lifecycles which could alter their value as evidence. Some specimens from each case are killed and preserved by immersion in boiling alcohol, and some are kept alive, sealed in a container along with a little raw meat or muscle tissue from the corpse itself. The types of insect found will depend on factors like climate, weather, altitude, and whether the body was buried or left in the open. A covering of soil stops some kinds of insects reaching the corpse, but many others, like burrowing beetles, are specially adapted for finding buried flesh – and in any case, insect infestation can occur before the body is buried. The most common egg-laying types of flies are houseflies (Muscidae), greenbottles (Lucilia), and particularly bluebottles (Calliphoridae). These lay eggs on moist parts of a body, like the eyes and mouth, or open wounds; the larvae hatch and feed on the body as they grow.

Bluebottles lay their eggs in sunlight on fresh meat, and in warm weather the eggs hatch into tiny maggots the next day. These maggots grow and shed their skins twice, so that by the fifth or sixth day they have become fat and fleshy; these third stage maggots eat voraciously for another five or six days, then curl up in a pupa case before becoming adult flies. Taking local temperatures into consideration, it is possible to date a corpse decomposing in this way to within a few days of death.

The Corpses in the Ravine

In 1935, the evidence of an entomologist was used in the celebrated case of Buck Ruxton, a doctor who used his skill in dissection to cut up the bodies of his victims. Mrs. Isabella Ruxton and Mary Rogerson, her maid, went missing from their home between the 14th and 15th of September 1935. Dr. Ruxton made various attempts to prevent enquiries about their disappearance by telling people they had gone visiting. He also suggested that Mary was pregnant, and that his wife had taken her away to have an abortion. But on the 29th of September 1935, the dismembered remains of two human bodies were found in a ravine at Moffat, a hundred miles from the Ruxtons' home.

The remains had suffered badly from putrefaction as well as being cut up, and so bluebottle larvae from the corpses were examined to determine when they had been dumped in the ravine. The largest larvae

The mummified body of a woman who had been murdered and buried in a warehouse full of sacking. The room was covered with the puparia of the blowfly Phormia Terrae Novae *which is locally active in early May, which helped to pinpoint the month of death.*

could not have been more than twelve days old, and as the bluebottle only lays its eggs on fresh meat during the day, it was shown that the remains had lain there for about a fortnight. Skilful work by pathologists finally identified the mixed up parts of the bodies as those of Mrs. Ruxton and Mary Rogerson, and the entomological evidence agreed well with the prosecution view that the women had been murdered on the 14th or 15th of September, and their bodies disposed of during the night of the 15th-16th September. The case against Dr. Ruxton involved many other strands of forensic evidence, as well as statements from many of the people whose suspicions he had tried to allay: not surprisingly, he was found guilty of the double murder.

Dr Zakaria Erzinclioglu, consultant entomologist to the Home Office, amid a selection of specimens.

The Effects of Insect Action

The action of insects can cause many changes to a body which may confuse those examining a corpse. The presence of maggots, for example, can raise the temperature of a body quite astoundingly: a temperature of 25.6°C (78°F) has been recorded in the maggot-infested tissues of a corpse six weeks dead. The heat produced by maggot infestation can also hasten the process of adipocere formation. Adipocere is caused by swelling and stiffening of the body fats, resulting in a swollen white substance which often remains attached to the bones and muscles long after the skin has rotted away. It forms during immersion in water or burial in moist conditions. This substance usually takes several months to develop, and its presence is sometimes used to indicate how long a person has been dead; however, the warming action of maggots can produce adipocere in as little as 3 weeks, making a corpse seem older than it actually is. Another way corpses can seem prematurely aged is through insect action on body tissue, and small areas of damage can be mistaken for wounds, while large amounts of tissue loss may make a corpse look more decomposed, and therefore older, than expected.

(top left)
The common bluebottle
Calliphora vicina,
*one of the most
widespread blowflies.*
(top right)
*Bluebottle larva at the
third instar, or stage, of
development, (5–6
days after the eggs were
laid).*
(bottom left)
*The barrel-shaped
pupae of the bluebottle,
from which the new flies
will emerge, 15–21
days after the eggs
were laid.*
(bottom right)
Musca Domestica,
the house fly.

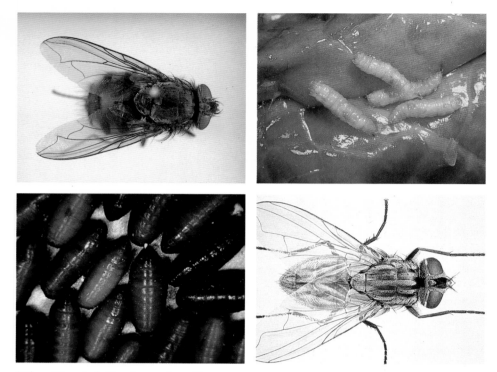

The Crucial Dating of a Corpse

In this way, insects had destroyed much of a body found in a shallow grave in Bracknell Woods on 28th June, 1964. Ironically, the body was found by two boys looking for maggots to use on a fishing trip; the remains found by the boys were maggot-ridden and disintegrating, and the police at first assumed that death had taken place six to eight weeks before. But the forensic pathologist assigned to the case had some experience of forensic entomology, and by examining the maggots' development he placed the death at only nine to twelve days previously. The police accordingly consulted their records of people who had gone missing about the 16th of June, and identified the body as that of Peter Thomas from Lydney in Gloucestershire. Enquiries led to the arrest of a Mr. William Brittle, who owed Mr. Thomas £2,000, and who said he had driven to Lydney and paid him on the very day of his disappearance – Brittle was charged with the murder. At his trial, the defence lawyers brought forward witnesses who claimed to have seen Mr. Thomas alive on several occasions – but according to the entomologists, by the time these sighting took place, Thomas' body was already being destroyed by maggots. In fact, the pathologist's opinion about the time of death was confirmed in court – by an entomologist called for the defence! The jury gave more credence to the entomological evidence than the witnesses' statements, and Brittle was given a life sentence for the murder of Peter Thomas. Without the clues provided by the entomologists, the original police estimate that the body was at least six weeks old might have been accepted, the dead man might never have been identified, and his killer might have gone unpunished.

Moths, Wasps and Larder Beetles

It is not only the action of flies and maggots which can help the forensic entomologist in illuminating the circumstances surrounding a death. The brown house moth eats skin and the internal organs of bodies, and can even digest hair; as we have seen, information about this moth helped reveal the truth about two mummified bodies, the mummy of Rhyl in 1960, and the baby found in a wall-cavity in the 1850s. Larder beetles also attack corpses, although not until three to six months after death, when the body fat has been converted to fatty acids and is rancid. It is not only flesh-eating species which are of use to the forensic entomologist, though; in the spring of 1985 a human skull was found in Tennessee, and inside the skull was a wasp nest. As wasps only build their nests in dry places, it was obvious that the skin and brain must have decayed away by the summer of 1984, leaving a dry cavity in which the wasps could construct their nest. This meant that death must have taken place in 1983 or before, giving time for the body tissues to disappear completely. This estimate was confirmed when more bones were discovered, including one vertebra from the backbone with a young tree growing through it – when cut through, the annual rings showed that this sapling was two years old, which tied in with the evidence of the wasp nest.

The common clothes moth and its larva which will eat the clothing, hair and even the dehydrated skin of a body in the right conditions.

So this somewhat unpleasant aspect of forensic science is nonetheless extremely useful, especially when human remains have been reduced to rather less than a whole body by deliberate dismemberment or natural putrefaction. The fatness of the grisly specimens handled by the forensic entomologist often bears a crucial silent witness to the time of their host's demise.

CHAPTER ELEVEN

Questioned Documents: Forgeries and Disguise

'It is a curious thing,' remarked Holmes, 'that a typewriter has really quite as much individuality as a man's handwriting. Unless they are quite new, no two of them write exactly alike. Some letters get more worn than others, and some wear only on one side...'

(A CASE OF IDENTITY)

On the face of it, the forensic document examiner has one of the least important and exciting jobs in the forensic science laboratory. While others are dealing with murder, robbery and assault, the document examiner sits at a desk, poring over sheets of paper. But those papers can be just as destructive as a knife or a gun, and their use is much more widespread – it is far more common to have a stolen cheque used in one's name than to be robbed at gunpoint.

The Implication of Documents

Questioned documents come in a variety of forms, from hold-up notes and ransom demands to anonymous threatening letters, from falsified business accounts to counterfeit banknotes. These days, it is not even unusual for graffiti-covered walls and doors to be examined in the hope of identifying the person who has defaced them; one individual can be responsible for an epidemic of graffiti, causing enormous damage to public buildings and monuments. Occasionally the document examiner is faced with really unexpected items like one brought in to the Metropolitan Police Forensic Science Laboratory – the mirror from a wardrobe door, on which a murderer had written using face cream. This proved very difficult to analyse, and the scientists could not extract much information from the writing, but it demonstrates the extreme end of the document examiner's work.

Handwriting

Handwriting is the most common type of evidence dealt with, and it offers the greatest scope for study. Our handwriting is a good means of identification, which is why our signatures are used on legal documents and cheques. Even the untrained eye can spot many examples of forgery, but skill and practice can produce a better fake which requires an expert to uncover it.

When we learn to write, we all copy from similar examples, and so we all produce similar results – and some of these common characteristics carry over into our adult writing. A great many people have superficially similar handwriting; but as we grow up our script develops individual variations, based on the need for speed or legibility. Sometimes our style is consciously cultivated to create a handwriting that we feel suits us. It is these features which allow the document examiner to assess whether one sample of writing matches another, because once we have acquired a set of characteristics, it needs a conscious and determined effort to change them. A person's natural handwriting is not always exactly the same, under different conditions, but it is always consistent.

Disguised handwriting

When comparing two samples of handwriting, some features at once indicate an attempt at disguised writing; these include slow, clumsy movement of the pen,

Examining a cheque for forgery with ultra-violet light.

stops and starts in unnatural places, shaky formation, careful 'repairing' of misformed letters, and obviously different letter-formation. Genuine writing is smooth, characterised by sweeping strokes to cross Ts, and to start and finish individual letters. There may be repairs to mistakes, but they will not be overly careful. An old or ill person's script might be slow and shaky, but it will still look natural and have a certain consistency throughout, whereas someone attempting forgery may also produce slow, shaky writing, but it will appear awkwardly formed and unnatural. It is easier to copy the general shape of someone's handwriting than incidentals like the starting and connecting strokes, writing slant and pen pressure – features which often depend on the structure of the hand itself – and many questioned documents reveal their true origin to the trained eye in this way.

Laser and Infra-red Detection

There are more sophisticated techniques, of course, for persuading handwritten documents to give up their secrets. All inks are not the same, for example, and special light source equipment can reveal the difference between apparently identical colours. The equipment consists of red, green and ultra-violet lights, which are shone at the sample in turn; viewed through an infra-red camera, some

Using laser light to show alterations or impeded signatures on a forged cheque.

inks appear luminescent, while others absorb the coloured light. So if a cheque for eight pounds has been altered to eighty pounds, the infra-red luminescence camera will show the addition of a 'y' on the end of 'eight', and a zero after the figure 8. The same technique can even be used to read words that have been crossed out or written over, providing that the two inks are different: by adjusting the light sources, the top ink can be made transparent while the ink beneath fluoresces through, revealing the underlying words.

Laser light can also be used in this way, and in fact helped to uncover writing on a most unusual 'document' – the palm of a policeman's hand. A few years ago, police forces near London were asked to look for a Dutch lorry which had been involved in an accident. A police constable in Essex saw a Dutch lorry thunder past him, and hastily wrote its registration number on the palm of his hand. He later checked the number and found it did not belong to the wanted lorry, so he washed the ink off his hand. The next day, the constable discovered that a second Dutch lorry was wanted, this time because it had been hi-jacked – but by now there was no trace of the registration number he had written on his skin. Under the Metropolitan Police Forensic Science laboratory's laser, however, the number could clearly be seen, and it matched that of the stolen lorry. The driver had already been interviewed, and according to his statement the lorry had not yet been stolen and was in another part of the county at the time the policeman reported seeing it. His story was disproved by the 'invisible' evidence on the constable's hand, and further enquiries revealed that the lorry's Dutch owners had staged the 'hi-jack' as an insurance fraud – which would have netted them half a million pounds.

The ESDA (Electrostatic Document Analysis) test
1. The pressure of writing leaves an impression on lower sheets.
2. The passing of electrostatic charges across the paper beneath, and then dusting with powder sensitive to the charges, reveals what had been written.

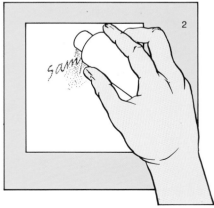

Electrostatic Images

The physical impressions made by a pen pressing on paper can go through several sheets, and this can frequently be used to show that a forger practised a false signature before signing a document. Very often when a cheque book is stolen, the thief practises signing the false name on the first cheque before trying to pay for something with the second, thus leaving the incriminating imprints of his earlier attempts all over the paper. On a very simple level, deep indentations can be revealed by shining a low angle light across the paper so the words appear as shadows.

Less obvious impressions can still be revealed by a more complicated process, which is best carried out in a room kept at 60-70% humidity. A thin sheet of plastic rather like clingfilm is placed on the suspect sheet of paper, and this plastic is given an electrostatic charge. As a result, an invisible electrostatic image of any indentations is produced on the plastic – the image is made visible by pouring black powder over the sheet so that it sticks to the electrostatic reproduction of the writing. (The powder is simply toner from any Xerox machine.) The excess powder is discarded, leaving a perfect image of any impressions in the paper. This technique is very useful for showing the order in which several sheets were written; each page should bear an imprint of the words on the previous page, and any gap in the sequence of impressions suggests that a page has been added at a later date.

Unravelling False Trails

The impression made by a pen was one of the pieces of evidence which helped clear up a trail of false clues left by an imaginative murderer. Unfortunately for him, however, he lacked thoroughness, and it was his very ingenuity that gave him away.

The man slipped away from his night shift and sneaked home, where he strangled his wife with the flex from the kettle. Afterwards he coolly arranged the scene, leaving various false clues which he hoped would point to an intruder having broken in and murdered his wife – then returned to work for the rest of the night. In the morning the man calmly invited a colleague back to his house for coffee, so there would be a witness to his 'finding' of the body.

Among the false clues he had left to fool the police were marks on a drainpipe where the non-existent intruder might have climbed up, with an open window at the top. He had also made an obscene note from newsprint letters stuck onto blue paper, and he left this beside the body. The backing paper from the note was analysed and found to be the cover from a book of raffle tickets, of a type commonly used in the area. In a drawer in the dining room, the police found just such a book of raffle tickets, with the cover missing – but this alone did not conclusively prove that the blue backing paper came from that particular book. However, the piece of blue paper was shown to bear the impression of a circular scribble, made while trying to get a ballpoint pen to work – and the first raffle ticket in the coverless book had an identical mark in its surface. This proved that the note had been made by

When a word has been obscured infra-red photography can often reveal what was written beneath .

The mystery letter on the Great Train Robbery received by the London Evening News in 1963. The typist was analysed as being an experienced male typist, and the typewriter was a 10–14 years old Remington.

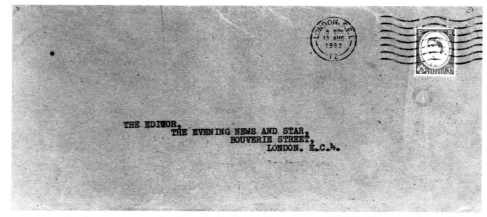

THE EDITOR,
THE EVENING NEWS AND STAR,
BOUVERIE STREET,
LONDON, E.C.4.

someone in the house, and a homicidal intruder was hardly likely to have sat down with newspapers and glue to produce his obscene note at the scene. Confronted with positive evidence that the killing was an inside job, the man confessed to the murder of his wife. He should have known better than to try and deceive the forensic science experts, though – because the man in question was himself a policeman.

The Idiosyncracies of Typewriters

As Sherlock Holmes knew even in the 1870's, it is not only handwriting that can be traced to its source; typewriters, too, have their stylistic idiosyncrasies which can be individually identified. Like guns and tools, typewriters sustain slight damage during use – not enough to warrant replacement, as this damage is often not even noticed by the user, but it is enough to show that a document was typed with a particular machine.

The letters become chipped and misaligned from the force with which they strike the roller, or they may bear tiny notches or protrusions caused by their original casting, and these minuscule faults are reproduced on the typed page. When magnified, such flaws become obvious, and because these unvarying faults can be scientifically measured, anonymous typed messages often prove to be even less 'anonymous' than handwritten ones. Handwriting is a variable process, and so the analysis of its characteristics will always be dependent on the experience of the person examining it, but typewriting can be positively matched with its parent machine.

No two typewriters ever produce the same result when examined under a microscope. Trained typists will also produce a more even type-pressure than an untrained hand.

CHAPTER TWELVE

Psychiatry: Unravelling the Criminal Mind

Several centuries ago, the mental disorders which modern psychiatrists study and treat were completely misunderstood. Inexplicable and apparently 'evil' acts were blamed on demonic possession, where a person was supposed to be taken over by a wicked spirit. Doctors tried to explain both physical and mental disease by pointing to imbalances between cool, hot, wet and dry elements in the body, but this was really no more scientific, and in the sixteenth century Paracelsus thought mental disorders were caused by heredity, head injury, poison – or worms and the influence of astral bodies. In the early nineteenth century, phrenologists suggested that the brain was a collection of organs, each with a separate psychological task; thus a thief would have an over-large region devoted to acquisition, but under-developed organs of morality. It was thought at the time that exercising or resting the appropriate organs would effect a cure, but by the second half of the century such ideas were discredited, and modern theories of psychiatry were being formulated.

A formidable array of bottles and test-tubes, with the pungent cleanly smell of hydrochloric acid, told me that he had spent his day in the chemical work which was so dear to him.
(A CASE OF IDENTITY)

Nowadays, the specialist in forensic psychiatry is most often called upon to give an opinion on the mental state of a suspect once caught, and this is an important part of the legal process which is often under-valued by the lay person. Conversely, great public interest has been shown in the more recent application of psychological expertise to the production of a character profile of a wanted man before he has been identified and caught. It sometimes seems that more confidence is placed in the accuracy of such pre-arrest predictions than in testimony based on an examination of the suspect in custody.

For example, the authorities used psychological profiling techniques in the hunt for Peter Sutcliffe, the 'Yorkshire Ripper', but when he came to trial, the psychiatrists' opinions were disregarded. Sutcliffe was responsible for the murder of at least thirteen women over five and a half years, and he was also charged with the attempted murder of seven others. Four psychiatrists (two speaking for the prosecution and two for the defence) agreed that he was mentally ill, probably suffering from paranoid schizophrenia, but a plea of diminished responsibility was disallowed by the court. He was tried under the assumption that the attacks were committed in a rational state of mind, found guilty and sent to prison. However, the psychiatrists were proved right in their assessment of Sutcliffe's mental state, for in prison his condition deteriorated until he had to be sent to Broadmoor special hospital – where he remains to this day.

Psychological Profiling

Psychological profiling is based on the criminal's behaviour at the scene of the crime, and it is used in very serious cases of sexual assault or murder, when the police believe the offence is part of a series of attacks. Multiple attacks are rare, but they also tend to be well-planned and therefore difficult to solve by conventional means – it is also difficult to comprehend the motives behind these ugly, violent crimes.

Frequently the perpetrator does not leave behind the normal types of evidence, but instead leaves a 'signature' or 'trademark' to his attack; such crimes are carried out to a set pattern, which not only links separate offences, but can also give clues to the man's personality and lifestyle. Serial killers use the same method to dispose of each of their victims; in one British case, the killer always asphyxiated his victims with a tourniquet and replaced the corpse's clothing after each offence.

An example of the handwriting as well as an insight into the mental state of Peter Sutcliffe, on a message found in his van.

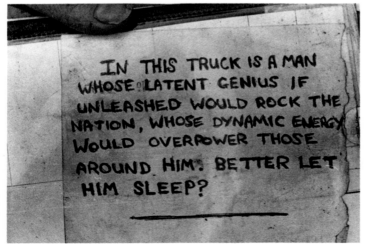

All sorts of information, like the way he spoke to surviving victims, the manner of attack, and any unusual behavioural signatures, are analysed to produce a description of the perpetrator – not a physical description, but a picture of the way his mind works and the way his life is organised. Once the police know what sort of person to look for, they may be able to see through the cloak of normality surrounding a serial rapist or murderer. We tend to picture such men as monsters, but they are often quiet and pleasant in their manner, showing no external signs of their terrible inner promptings.

The NCAVC in Virginia

Both the British police and the FBI in America operate psychological profiling programmes, and the American system is the most developed and successful in the world. Based at the FBI's Behavioural Science Unit in Virginia is the National Centre for the Analysis of Violent Crime, which handles 1,000 cases from around the world each year; the NCAVC helped the British police produce a profile of Peter Sutcliffe in the Yorkshire Ripper case.

The amassed information from these cases has enabled the investigators to draw up some uncannily accurate profiles from apparently perplexing crime scenes. In 1979 a woman's body was found, savagely mutilated, on the roof of a New York block of flats; the body was identified as that of Francine Evelson, a teacher who lived in the block. It was apparent that the killer had spent a long time on the roof because the mutilations to the body were extensive, and because he even had to defecate on the roof. When the FBI was called in, an instant profile was produced from the information at the scene, viewed in the light of previous cases. The wanted man was white, because the victim was white and serial killers almost always strike within their own racial group; he lived or worked in the same block of flats, because he had spent so much time on the roof that he must have regarded it as his own territory. FBI agent John Douglas also felt they should be looking for an unmarried man of between twenty-five and thirty, who collected pornographic and detective magazines. If the man had links with the building, he must already have been interviewed by the police – so they reviewed the people they had spoken to, and one Carmine Calabro stuck out like a sore thumb. He exactly fitted the FBI's description, and was arrested for the killing.

The Psychological Background

The characteristics at the scene of a crime can speak volumes about the perpetrator, but investigators have found another way to get inside the mind of the serial killer. Since 1979, American serial murderers in custody have been questioned about their backgrounds, their motives and their methods, to build up a chillingly detailed picture of the 'typical' serial killer. For despite their often weird and revolting criminal signatures, like particular mutilations or cannibalism, these men show a remarkable degree of similarity in some respects.

They are usually male, white, middle class and in their late twenties or early thirties, with a high IQ but a poor academic and work record. There is often a family background of drug or alcohol addiction, child abuse and psychiatric illness; the father may have deserted the family or died, but if he was there it was usually as a distant, undemonstrative presence. Multiple sexual killers tend to be sexually inexperienced, preferring solitary sexual activities like pornography, masturbation and voyeurism to any kind of relationship – but sex is by no means the only object behind such attacks. Chris Hanson would pick up prostitutes, fly them out into the wilds in his plane, then hunt them down like animals; the thrill he found in the chase and the kill led him to murder 187 women.

These men are also likely to be obsessed with police work and the detection process, reading crime stories and acting out the role of a lawman in their crimes: the two cousins who were jointly responsible for the attacks ascribed to the 'Hillside Strangler' posed as policemen in order to lure young women into their car. Instead of taking them to the police station, they would drive the victims to one of their houses, sexually assault and strangle them, then dump the bodies. Prostitutes and hitch hikers are the most common victims of such killers, because they expect to attract police attention and would get into a 'police car' without question.

Another killer fascinated with the role of the police was Edmund Kemper, a 6 foot 9 inch serial killer from Montana who fits the FBI profile well. His parents divorced when he was seven, leaving him a bitter child, strangely obsessed with the relationship between death and eroticism. When his sister dared him to kiss a teacher, seven year old Ed replied 'I would have to kill her first'. At night he sometimes stood over his mother's sleeping body and pretended to stab her with a kitchen knife. At fifteen he went to stay with his paternal grandparents on their ranch, where he killed them both; as a result he was held in custody for some years, but was released at the age of twenty-one. During the next year he killed, molested and mutilated a series of women students, and often practised necrophilia on the bodies. All this time he remained a police fan, and even drank at a policeman's bar, chatting with the officers. Finally, on Good Friday 1973, he decapitated his mother – then surrendered to the police, because he felt no more need to kill.

Gerald Schaffer actually made it into the police force, which made it easy for him to carry out his preferred method of attack. He would offer lifts to hitch hikers, drive them to a lonely spot and hang them. Schaffer was a necrophiliac, but he also enjoyed seeing his victims urinate before they died, so he would purposely make them drink beforehand. Detectives cannot be sure, but he may have claimed over twenty-four victims. Necrophilia is among the more comprehensible habits of such men – some serial killers remove parts of their victims' bodies, especially the sexual organs, and preserve these grisly souvenirs by freezing or pickling.

The sorts of psychotic or psycho-sexual tendencies which lead people to commit these terrible acts do not result in total mental disablement; in the rest of their lives, they may appear normal, friendly and articulate. Such men are often creative and adaptable, and these traits spill over into their criminal acts, enabling them to plan and carry out their attacks with great skill and cunning. Many practice by stalking a potential victim, weapon in hand, but pull out at the last moment. They are often of above-average intelligence, which helps them evade high-level police manhunts – indeed, they frequently follow their own cases and are extremely co-operative with the police so they can pick up inside information about the hunt. Sometimes they even feed their feelings of superior intelligence by taunting the authorities with messages containing clues to their identity.

The Problems of Treatment and Rehabilitation

There is quite a deep divide between psychiatrists, even those involved in the evaluation and treatment of apprehended criminals, and the officers who run psychological profiling programmes in Britain and the United States. Psychiatrists are committed to counselling and treating the mentally sick, whereas the law enforcement agencies' main concern is to find the offender and stop the bloodshed. Indeed, the psychological abnormalities found in serial killers and violent multiple rapists are probably unclassifiable and are certainly untreatable within our present understanding of the human mind.

This is the view of Theodore (Ted) Bundy, a graduate in law and psychology, and himself the killer of over twenty young women:

"If anybody's looking for pat answers, forget it. If there were, the psychiatrists would have cleared this up years ago."

So far, forensic psychiatrists from law enforcement agencies on both sides of the Atlantic would readily admit to having only a rudimentary understanding of the most disturbed criminal minds. Their major weapons against the crimes of such perpetrators are their detection facilities and skills; but against the root causes for the most terrible and humanly baffling crimes we still have no defence.

CHAPTER THIRTEEN

Toxicology:
Analysing Drugs and Poisons

If you are going back to Pitt Street you might see Mr. Horace Harker. Tell him from me that I have quite made up my mind, and that it is certain that a dangerous homicidal lunatic with Napoleonic delusions was in his house last night.

(THE SIX NAPOLEONS)

Toxicology is the study of poisons, and the job of the forensic toxicologist is to detect, identify and quantify poisons in body tissues or fluids; the samples involved may come from a post mortem, or from a living person. A poison can be defined as a substance which causes ill-health or death when taken in a sufficiently large quantity, and it is the quantity as much as the poison itself which is important. The sixteenth century physician Paracelsus often followed the superstitious beliefs of his day, but he laid the ground for the modern science of toxicology when he wrote that:

"All substances are poisons; there is none that is not a poison. The right dose differentiates a poison and a remedy."

Significant amounts of even apparently innocuous substances can have fatal results, while small doses of a 'poison' like cyanide can be taken without ill-effect. In fact, a little cyanide is necessary for the body to produce vitamin B12, and small quantities of the poison are also produced and absorbed during cigarette smoking. Slight traces of some heavy metals like lead, mercury and arsenic, which are toxic in high doses, are also often found in the body. Although these are not strictly needed by the body in the way that cyanide is, low concentrations of these metals are absorbed from the general environment and can be tolerated without harm. An acceptable level of lead in the blood, for instance, would be up to 0.2 milligrammes per litre, but more than 0.7mg per litre would cause serious illness and possibly death.

The Tolerance Levels of the Human Body
The effect of a substance on any given person is always influenced by their age, weight, sex and general state of health, so the same dose can affect two people in completely different ways – especially if one

of them has developed a tolerance to the substance. 'Tolerance' means that the body is less responsive to a poison or drug because it has previously been exposed to the substance, usually over a long period; thus hardened drinkers can absorb a great deal of alcohol without apparently coming to harm, and drug addicts will have to keep increasing their 'fix' to produce the same effect. Indeed, the same level of alcohol or drugs could very well kill someone who was not used to such large doses of what are essentially poisons. It is even possible to build up a tolerance to arsenic in this way, by gradually increasing the amount taken, until a normally fatal dose can be swallowed harmlessly; a would-be murderer might find that if a first attempt failed, it would need an even greater dose to dispatch the victim in future.

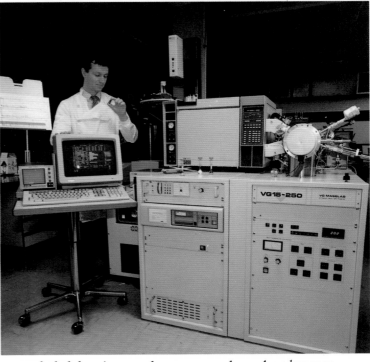

A modern mass spectrometer used to identify drugs.

So the concept of what constitutes poison or a lethal dose is a very loose one, and the toxicologist has to reach conclusions within wide limits. The forensic toxicologist also assesses the effects of drugs, including alcohol, on the bodies of victims and suspects of crime, with a view to explaining their patterns of behaviour as they relate to the case.

Suicide Poisoning

In the U.K. about 120,000 cases of poisoning are admitted to hospitals each year, and most of these patients are successfully treated. Of those who do not survive, foul play is rarely a factor in the death. Intentional homicidal poisoning is mercifully rare, and the majority of a forensic toxicologist's workload centres around drug abuse, accidental poisoning, and suicide.

Suicide is the most common type of death by poisoning, and the methods used are characteristic. Carbon monoxide from the exhaust gases of a car is frequently used by suicides because it is easily obtainable, simple to use and painless. The gas is inhaled and affects the blood; normally, oxygen is transported around the body by haemoglobin in the blood, but carbon monoxide is three hundred times more attractive in this way than oxygen, and it combines with the haemoglobin instead of the oxygen. This means the blood cannot take up enough oxygen, and the victim dies of oxygen deprivation. Carbon monoxide poisoning is easily detectable by measuring the concentration of the gas dissolved in the blood, and the characteristic pink colour of the victim.

An overdose of prescription drugs is another common method of suicide, and a lethal cocktail of different drugs is often taken to ensure success. Because the action of poisonous chemicals is usually hidden within the body, many drug-related suicides are at first thought to be the result of accident or foul play, and the suspicion of poisoning is only raised by the presence of pills or capsules at the scene. In one such case, a man was found dead in his toilet, and it appeared he had been murdered; however, one Tuinal capsule was found lying on the floor of the room – it was almost missed against the bright pattern of the carpet. This discovery pointed the forensic scientists in the right direction, and after chemical analysis of his tissues the man's death was shown to be caused by an overdose of Tuinal.

Fake Suicides

Sometimes attempts are made to fake a suicidal poisoning as a cover-up for murder, but this sort of deception can be detected in two ways. Firstly, the circumstances of the 'suicide' may be suspicious to the experienced investigator – suicides have typical ways of doing things, which the murderer will not be aware of. For example, genuine suicides will almost always remove their glasses before committing the act, and they rarely use an uncomfortable or unpleasant position. If the circumstances surrounding a faked suicide do not arouse suspicion, the post mortem will reveal the true cause of death.

A common disguise for murder is suicide by carbon monoxide poisoning, for instance, but the post mortem will show that there is no gas dissolved in the blood, so the victim must already have stopped breathing.

Both the unlikely circumstances at the scene and the post mortem results helped to solve one case of murder disguised as suicide. Some years ago, before the widespread use of natural gas, the mains supply was provided by poisonous coal gas, which contained carbon monoxide. Neighbours smelled this gas coming from the ground floor of a house where a woman lived alone. She was found dead with her head in the gas oven, and a local doctor attributed the death to coal gas poisoning; it was assumed she had committed suicide because she was depressed at separating from her husband. But the woman's head was found lying on a dirty pan in the oven, an uncomfortable and greasy position which was highly uncharacteristic of a true suicide. In addition, the ambulance staff who recovered the body noticed a mark on the woman's neck, which was examined at the post mortem. It was revealed thatthere was no carbon monoxide in the blood, so the woman must have already been dead when her head was placed in the oven – the real cause of death was strangulation with the collar of her blouse. The dead woman's husband had an alibi for the time of her death, but he was arrested and finally confessed to killing his wife and faking her suicide.

It is often more difficult to detect homicidal poisoning, because by the nature of the crime it is usually premeditated: one cannot just approach the victim and say "swallow this". So the killer will usually have had time to plan the attack and arrange the scene as naturally as possible. A further complication is that poisons rarely cause obvious or characteristic changes to body tissues, so if there is no suspicion of poisoning, the pathologist conducting the post mortem may not take any samples for chemical analysis.

Some Symptoms of Poisoning

Some of the poisons we automatically think of when considering the possibility of murder produce symptoms almost indistinguishable from those of natural illness. Strychnine poisoning results in convulsions which can be mistaken for those caused by tetanus. The availability of

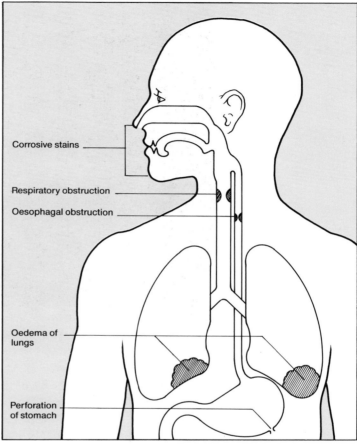

Corrosive stains

Respiratory obstruction

Oesophagal obstruction

Oedema of lungs

Perforation of stomach

The results of corrosive poisoning by the irritant fumes or liquids of acids, ammonia, or caustic soda and potash.

strychnine is closely controlled, but it can be obtained in the form of medicines. Murderers have been known to disguise its bitter taste – with grave consequences for their victims. Within a few minutes the muscles start to twitch and the chest feels tight; suddenly the body becomes quite rigid, the back arches, and a grim smile is fixed on the face. After a moment or two this spasm ends and the body relaxes, but the convulsion will recur again and again – death results from exhaustion a few hours later. The main difference between tetanus convulsions and those due to strychnine poisoning is that the latter makes the chest fixed and immobile, while tetanus produces a greater spasm in the jaw.

Arsenical substances also produce confusing symptoms which can prevent deliberate attempts at poisoning being spotted – but arsenic is easily detectable in the body tissues after death, which may mean that a successful murderer is in greater danger of discovery than an unsuccessful one. Chronic poisoning over a length of

'Cooking' up fragments of human tissue in a toxicologist's laboratory in order to extract drug samples.

time causes general symptoms of ill-health like loss of appetite, weight loss and occasional vomiting; it also produces a brown pigmentation of the skin, like freckles, known as melanosis. One large dose of arsenic, usually hidden in food, results in what appears to be severe gastro-enteritis, with abdominal pain and vomiting. This is followed by diarrhoea, cramps in the limbs, and muscular twitching or convulsions; death can occur in only a few hours, though the victim may last for several days.

In 1949, a Mrs. Radford was dying of pulmonary tuberculosis in a Surrey hospital – however, she was dying too slowly for her husband's liking, so he decided to speed the process by poisoning her with arsenic. As a laboratory assistant he had no difficulty in obtaining enough potassium arsenite to kill his wife, and he hid the poison in fruit pies and drinks that he took into the hospital as gifts for her. (The fruit pies were later found to contain 162.5 mg of potassium arsenite, a lethal dose.) The hospital staff attributed Mrs. Radford's symptoms to her natural disease, and it was not until after her death that chance revealed the true facts of the case, that her demise was accelerated by acute arsenical poisoning.

Cyanide and hydrocyanic acid (prussic acid) are very fast-acting poisons, but fairly painless in their effects. They work by preventing the body tissues taking up the oxygen circulating in the blood, and death is caused by central respiratory and circulatory paralysis. Cyanide produces certain recognisable symptoms, but because it acts so rapidly it is often difficult to save a victim even if the poison is identified – cyanide typically causes death in ten to twenty minutes, but with hydrocyanic acid death can be instantaneous. In one witnessed case of suicide, a laboratory worker drank from a bottle of the acid and fell to the floor even as he took the bottle from his lips; his breathing stopped within seconds. As cyanide prevents the uptake

Analysis of illicit amphetamine powders.

of oxygen from the blood, the red blood cells do not lose their colour, and the blood, skin and tissues of a victim will therefore be flushed and pink. Another characteristic sign of this poison is the smell of bitter almonds which lingers in the mouth, or comes from the opened skull at the post mortem.

Poisoning Revealed at the Post-Mortem

The forensic pathologist should always open the skull before the body cavity, because odours like the bitter almond scent of cyanide are easily masked by stronger smells. The sense of smell is not only useful for detecting the presence of cyanide; substances like alcohol, ether and chloroform can also be detected in this way. An example of this phenomenon occurred when the body of a girl was found on her bed, with no apparent cause for the death; when the skull was opened, the pathologist noticed an unusual smell, and analysis of the tissue showed this was the odour of carbon tetrachloride. Enquiries among the girl's friends revealed that she often sniffed cleaning fluid containing this chemical, and a sealed bottle of the fluid was found in her room. It was deduced that she had spilt some of the fluid on the bedclothes, re-sealed the bottle, and then been gradually overcome by the vapours from the evaporating cleaning fluid.

Some substances leave more obvious signs on the body; when a corpse has lain in one position for some time after death, the blood gravitates to the lower areas of the body, producing a purple-blue staining effect called post mortem lividity, or hypostasis – but in cases of carbon monoxide poisoning, this lividity is a characteristic cherry-red colour. Acute cases of cyanide poisoning show bright pink patches of lividity, and potassium chlorate causes brown staining.

The presence of whole or partially absorbed tablets in the mouth or stomach of a corpse suggests the likelihood of poisoning, usually suicidal in origin, but appearances can be deceptive. The empty capsules which contained barbiturates are sometimes mistaken for grape skins or berries in the stomach; in 1955, a five month old baby boy died, and what appeared to be red berries were found in his body at the post mortem. This cause of death was at first accepted, but a later exhumation of the body revealed that the 'berries' were in fact the remains of Seconal capsules, and that the child had been murdered with the drug.

Brightly coloured paper squares impregnated with LSD. Each square is sucked to provide an individual 'trip'.

91

Biotransformation

Another problem facing the forensic toxicologist is a process called biotransformation; this is when the body converts an ingested chemical into an new and different compound. The resulting chemical is known as a metabolite, and it may be the only indication that the original substance was present in the body. Cocaine and heroin are both very quickly broken down into their respective metabolites, benzoylecgonine and morphine, and so the forensic scientist will have to look for these secondary substances rather than the drugs themselves. Metabolites are usually less toxic than their parent chemicals, though this is not always the case; ethyl alcohol is transformed into nothing worse than acetic acid, but methanol converts into a more poisonous chemical, formaldehyde.

A variety of tests exists for the identification of drugs and poisonous substances, either in tissues or fluid from a body, or in the form in which they were administered; these techniques include infra-red spectrography and gas chromatography, which we have already considered, and mass spectrometry. A mass spectrometer is exquisitely sensitive, looking at fragments of the individual molecules in a sample to make an identification. The suspect sample is dissolved in a solvent and a chemical marker is added, before a tiny amount is injected into the machine – as little as a thousandth of a millilitre of the solution. This is passed through a gas chromatograph to separate the sample into its individual components, and these are fed into the vacuum chamber of the mass spectrometer. Here, the sample is bombarded by a beam of electrons, which breaks each molecule into a

The poisoned umbrella used to kill the Bulgarian dissident writer Georgi Markov, in 1978, showing the pellet that contained the deadly ricin poison.

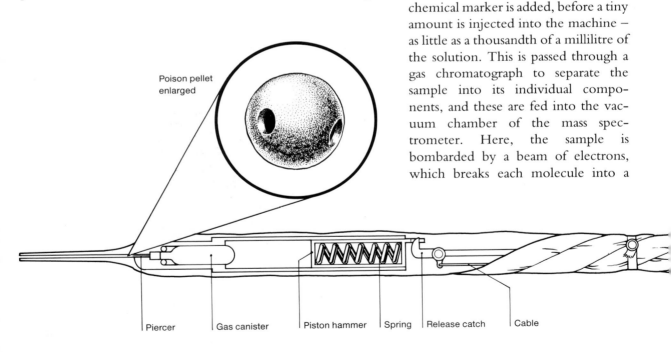

Poison pellet enlarged

Piercer   Gas canister   Piston hammer   Spring   Release catch   Cable

positively-charged particle called an ion. (An ion is the part of a molecule left after thenegatively-charged electron has been removed.) The resulting ions are shot through the analyser, which detects them according to their atomic mass. The 'mass spectrum' produced by the equipment shows the mass-to-charge ratio of the individual fragments of molecules: the resulting information is a bit like the pieces of a molecular jigsaw, which the forensic scientist can fit back together to identify the original chemical compound.

A Poison Casualty of the Cold War

But even with all the sensitive equipment and accumulated knowledge at their disposal, forensic toxicologists can still find poisons elusive and frustrating to deal with. In 1981, the exiled Bulgarian broadcaster Georgi Markov was murdered with an unidentified poison – while walking down a London street, an unknown man jabbed him in the leg with the tip of an umbrella. Two days later, Markov died in agony, and it was not until a pathologist examined his body that a tiny metal pellet was found embedded in his leg. (The wound it had caused looked like an insect bite, and had previously been overlooked.)

The pellet was hollow, pierced with holes to let out a poison, and it could have held no more than 0.2 milligrams of the mystery substance. Since it would have taken a thousand times more arsenic (about 200 milligrams) to kill Markov, this unknown poison must have been incredibly toxic. Based on this calculation, the forensic toxicologists have eliminated almost all known poisons: the only possibility was one of the phytotoxins, extremely poisonous substances derived from plants. Of these, the likeliest culprit is ricin, which is found in the hard outer covering of castor oil seeds. This toxin causes many accidental poisonings in countries where the plant grows, and these cases are easily diagnosed by the presence of seeds in the stomach – but the minuscule quantity believed to have killed Markov was undetectable in body tissues using the techniques available at the time. Modern advances have brought the possibility of such detection closer, but thankfully there have been no cases of ricin poisoning on which to try the new advances in toxicology.

As a post script to the Markov case, the Bulgarian authorities have recently admitted that their secret police were involved in the murder, so perhaps the forensic scientists will soon have their opinion confirmed by the only people who know the whole truth about Markov's death.

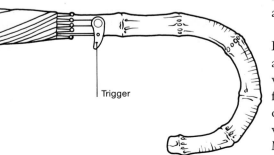

Trigger

Index

Index

Picture Credits